It's another great book from CGP...

Physics exams can seem daunting — especially if you're not sure what to expect.
But they're less stressful if you've done plenty of realistic practice in advance.

Happily, this book (which includes a **free** Online Edition)
is packed with exam-style questions for every topic. It even includes
two complete practice exams to fully prepare you for the real thing.

How to get your free online edition

Want to read this book on your computer or tablet?
Just go to **cgpbooks.co.uk/extras** and enter this code...

3928 3869 1313 9239

By the way, this code only works for one person. If somebody else has used
this book before you, they might have already claimed the online edition.

What CGP is all about

Our sole aim here at CGP is to produce the highest quality books —
carefully written, immaculately presented and dangerously close to being funny.

Then we work our socks off to get them out to you
— at the cheapest possible prices.

Contents

✓ Use the tick boxes to check off the topics you've completed.

How to Use This Book...1
Exam Tips..2

Section 1 — Forces and Motion

Velocity and Acceleration 3
D-T and V-T Graphs..5
Mass, Weight and Gravity..7
Forces and Friction..8
Investigating Motion..9
Terminal Velocity...10
The Three Laws of Motion..12
Combining Forces..14
Stopping Distances...15
Momentum and Collisions..16
Turning Forces and Centre of Gravity...18
Principle of Moments...19
Hooke's Law..20
Gravity and the Universe..21
Orbital Speed..22

Section 2 — Electricity

Safe Plugs...24
Fuses and Circuit Breakers...25
Energy and Power in Circuits..26
Circuits — the Basics..28
Resistance and V = I × R...29
LDRs, Thermistors and LEDs..31
Series and Parallel Circuits...32
Charge, Voltage and Energy Change...33
Static Electricity..34
Static Electricity — Examples..36

Section 3 — Waves

Waves — The Basics..38
Wave Behaviour and EM Waves...40
Uses of Electromagnetic Waves..41
Dangers of Electromagnetic Waves...44
Reflection of Waves...45
Refraction of Waves...46
Refractive Index and Snell's Law..47
Refractive Index and Critical Angles...49
Analogue and Digital Signals..50
Sound Waves...51

Section 4 — Energy Resources and Energy Transfer

Conservation of Energy 53

Efficiency 54

Energy Transfers 55

Sankey Diagrams 56

Heat Transfer 58

Heat Convection 59

Reducing Energy Transfers 60

Work and Power 61

Kinetic and Gravitational Potential Energy 63

Non-Renewable Energy and Power Stations 65

Nuclear, Wind and Geothermal Energy 66

Solar and Wave Energy 67

Generating Electricity Using Water 68

Section 5 — Solids, Liquids and Gases

Pressure and Density 69

Changes of State 71

Particle Theory and Temperature in Gases 72

Particle Theory and Pressure in Gases 73

Section 6 — Magnetism and Electromagnetism

Magnets and Magnetic Fields 74

Electromagnetism 75

The Motor Effect 77

Electric Motors and Loudspeakers 78

Electromagnetic Induction 79

Transformers 81

Section 7 — Radioactivity and Particles

Radioactivity 83

The Three Kinds of Radioactivity 84

Alpha Scattering and Nuclear Equations 85

Half-Life 87

Uses of Nuclear Radiation 89

Risks from Nuclear Radiation 91

Nuclear Fission 92

Practice Papers

Practice Paper 1P 93

Practice Paper 2P 117

Answers 132

Equations Page 148

How to get answers for the Practice Papers
Your free Online Edition of this book includes all the answers for Practice Papers 1P & 2P.
(Just flick back to the previous page to find out how to get hold of your Online Edition.)

Published by CGP

Editors:
Jane Ellingham, Rachael Marshall, Matteo Orsini Jones, Charlotte Whiteley, Sarah Williams.

Contributors:
Frederick Langridge

With thanks to Ian Francis, Glenn Rogers and Karen Wells for the proofreading.
With thanks to Catherine Davis for the reviewing.

Data used to construct stopping distance diagram on page 101 from the Highway Code.
© Crown Copyright re-produced under the terms of the Open Government licence
http://www.nationalarchives.gov.uk/doc/open-government-licence/

ISBN: 978 1 84762 696 7

Clipart from Corel®
Printed by Elanders Ltd, Newcastle upon Tyne

Based on the classic CGP style created by Richard Parsons.

How to Use This Book

- Hold the book <u>upright</u>, approximately <u>50 cm</u> from your face, ensuring that the text looks like <u>this</u>, not ̄s̄īẖ̄t̄. Alternatively, place the book on a <u>horizontal</u> surface (e.g. a table or desk) and sit adjacent to the book, at a distance which doesn't make the text too small to read.

- In case of emergency, press the two halves of the book together <u>firmly</u> in order to close.

- Before attempting to use this book, familiarise yourself with the following <u>safety information</u>:

> The questions are arranged into topics, so you can get exam practice on exactly the bit of your course that you want.

14

| PAPER 2 |

Combining Forces

1 Most quantities can be divided into two groups: scalars and vectors.

a) Describe the difference between a scalar and a vector quantity.

....

....
[2]

> There are stamps to show you which questions test Paper 2 material. If the stamp is by the topic title, the whole topic tests Paper 2 material.

> There are answer lines for you to write your answers on. For calculation questions, there's also space for you to do your working.

b) Which of the following is a **vector**? Place a cross in the appropriate box to indicate your answer.

☐ speed   ☐ distance   ☐ mass   ☐ force
[1]

c) Which of the following is a **scalar**? Place a cross in the appropriate box to indicate your answer.

○ 14 kg   ○ 300 kN down   ○ 24 m/s west   ○ 1 m/s² up
[1]

[Total 4 marks]

> Sometimes you'll be asked to place a cross in a box, or fill in parts of a table.

> Some questions have a bit of the working done for you, to help get you started on trickier topics. You won't get this in the exam though I'm afraid.

The refractive index in glass for violet light is 1.528. Calculate the angle θ shown in the diagram.

Angle of incidence for violet light = *i* = ...

$\sin r = \frac{\sin i}{n}$ (where *r* is the angle of refraction for violet light and *n* is the refractive index for violet light of the glass block).

$= \frac{\sin ....}{1.528}$ = ... ⇒ *r* = ...

θ = ... − ....

= ....

θ = ... °
[4]

> These contain handy tips to help you with specific questions.

> You're told how many marks each question part is worth, and then the total for the whole question.

ii) Calculate the maximum depth from the surface of the water that the watch can be used at.

> Remember that the pressure is in kPa. You'll need to convert it to do this calculation.

Maximum depth = ... m
[3]

[Total 8 marks]

> Exam Practice Tips give you hints to help with answering exam questions.

Exam Practice Tip

It's important to remember with questions like the last one that it's the height **difference** that matters. If you climb to an altitude of 4000 m and want to know the pressure difference from when you started, the first thing to ask is "what was my initial altitude?" Don't just plug 4000 into the equation if you didn't start at O.

Score
[ ]
21

> Use the answers at the back of the book to mark each page. Then you can find your score out of the total for the topic. If you're not doing the Paper 2 questions, the total score for some topics will be lower.

Section 5 — Solids, Liquids and Gases   ☹ ☐   ☺ ☐   ☺ ☐

> Tick the box that matches how confident you feel with the questions in each topic. This should help show you where you need to focus your revision.

Exam Tips

Edexcel Certificate Exam Stuff

1) You have to do two exams for the Edexcel Certificate in Physics — Paper 1 and Paper 2 (ingenious).

2) Paper 1 is 2 hours long and worth 120 marks.

3) Paper 2 is just 1 hour long, and it's worth 60 marks.

4) Some material in the specification will only be tested in Paper 2.
The questions that cover Paper 2 material in this book are marked with a stamp.

If you're doing the International GCSE in Physics, it works in exactly the same way — so you'll do two papers too.

There are a Few Golden Rules

1) **Always, always, always make sure you read the question properly.**
For example, if the question asks you to give your answer in m³, don't give it in cm³.

2) **Look at the number of marks a question is worth.**
The number of marks gives you a pretty good clue of how much to write.
So if a question is worth four marks, make sure you write four decent points. And there's no point writing an essay for a question that's only worth one mark — it's just a waste of your time.

3) **Write your answers as clearly as you can.**
If the examiner can't read your answer you won't get any marks, even if it's right.

Obeying these Golden Rules will help you get as many marks as you can in the exam — but they're no use if you haven't learnt the stuff in the first place. So make sure you revise well and do as many practice questions as you can.

4) **Use specialist vocabulary.**
You know the words I mean — the silly sciencey ones, like fission and convection. Examiners love them.

5) **Pay attention to the time.**
The amount of time you've got for each paper means you should spend about a minute per mark.
So if you're totally, hopelessly stuck on a question, just leave it and move on to the next one.
You can always go back to it at the end if you've got enough time.

6) **Show each step in your calculations.**
You're less likely to make a mistake if you write things out in steps. And even if your final answer's wrong, you'll probably pick up some marks if the examiner can see that your method is right.

You Need to Understand the Command Words

Command words are the words in a question that tell you what to do.
If you don't know what they mean, you might not be able to answer the questions properly.

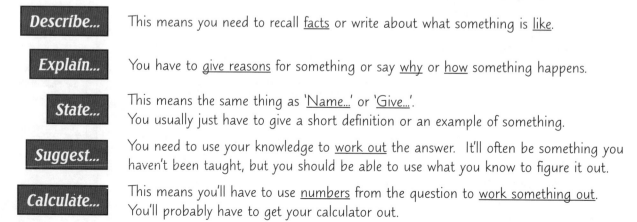

Describe...   This means you need to recall facts or write about what something is like.

Explain...   You have to give reasons for something or say why or how something happens.

State...   This means the same thing as 'Name...' or 'Give...'.
You usually just have to give a short definition or an example of something.

Suggest...   You need to use your knowledge to work out the answer. It'll often be something you haven't been taught, but you should be able to use what you know to figure it out.

Calculate...   This means you'll have to use numbers from the question to work something out.
You'll probably have to get your calculator out.

Velocity and Acceleration

1   A cyclist travels 1500 m from his house to his local shops in 300 seconds.

a) State the equation linking average speed, distance moved and time taken.

distance = speed × ~~from~~ time

[1]

b) Calculate the cyclist's average speed during his journey.

Average speed = ...5....... m/s

[2]

c) On the return home, the cyclist accelerates from 2.0 m/s with a steady acceleration of 2.4 m/s². Calculate the time it takes the cyclist to reach 10 m/s.

$$= \frac{(\cancel{2.4}^{10} - 2.)}{2.4}$$

Time = ...3.3....... s

[4]

[Total 7 marks]

2   A coin is rolled along a balcony edge at a steady speed of 0.46 m/s before falling off the edge after 2.4 seconds. It then accelerates due to gravity and hits the ground after 8.0 seconds at a speed of 78.4 m/s. Assume no air resistance acts on the coin.

a) Calculate how far the coin rolls before falling off the edge of the balcony.

0.46×2.4

Distance = ...1.1....... m

[3]

b) Calculate the acceleration of the coin during its fall.

$$\frac{(78.4 - 0.46)}{8}$$

Acceleration = ...9.7425....... m/s²

[3]

[Total 6 marks]

3 A model car company produces battery-powered model cars.
Their latest model accelerates from rest to 20 m/s in 3.5 s, and has a top speed of 25 m/s.

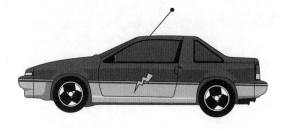

a) Calculate the acceleration of the model car during these 3.5 seconds.

$$\left(\frac{20 - 0}{\cancel{top} - \cancel{vo}}\right)$$
$$\frac{}{3.5}$$

5.7

Acceleration = ... m/s²

[3]

b) Calculate how fast the car would be moving if it travelled with the acceleration in part a) from rest for 1.5 seconds.

$$1.43 = \frac{(x - 0)}{1.5}$$ 5.

$$1.43 = \frac{x}{1.5}$$

$$1.4\, x = 1.3 \quad x = \frac{1.5}{14}$$

3.8

Velocity = ... m/s

[3]

[Total 6 marks]

4 A tractor ploughing a field accelerates at 3 m/s² for 1.2 seconds, after which its velocity is 5 m/s.

a) Calculate the tractor's velocity before it started accelerating.

$$3 = \frac{(5 - x)}{1.2}$$

Velocity = ...1.4...... m/s

[4]

b) As the tractor approaches the end of the field, it turns at a constant speed until it's facing the opposite direction. State whether the tractor accelerates during this time and explain your answer.

...No because acceleration needs a change...
...in speed and here they only change direction...
= change in velocity

[1]

[Total 5 marks]

Exam Practice Tip

Acceleration and velocity questions are exam favourites so make sure you're happy doing all the questions in this topic. You won't be given any of the formulas you've used on these last two pages in the exam, so make sure you really know them back to front, how to rearrange them and the units of each of the terms.

Score

24

D-T and V-T Graphs

1 A student walks to football training but finds she has left her boots at home. She turns around and walks back home, where she spends 50 seconds looking for the boots. Below is a distance-time graph for her journey.

a) Use the graph to find the time it took for the student to walk to training.

Time = ...300..... s
[1]

b) State whether the student walked to training at a steady speed. Explain how you know.

.....yes, the student is walking at a stedy pace because the line is straight meaning the speed doesn't altar.....
[2]

c) Use the graph to calculate the student's average speed as she walked to football training.

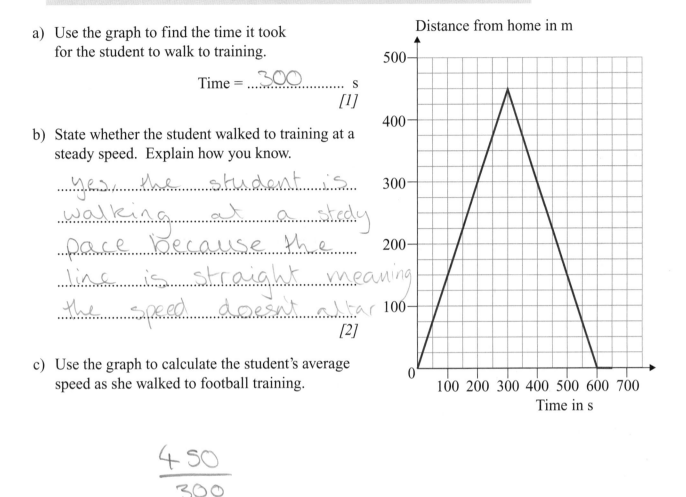

$$\frac{450}{300}$$

Average speed = ...1.5..... m/s
[3]

d) The student returns home after training in a car. During the journey, the car constantly accelerates for 10 s to overtake another vehicle and then travels at a constant speed for a further 30 s.

On the axes below, sketch a velocity-time graph to show the motion of the car during this time.

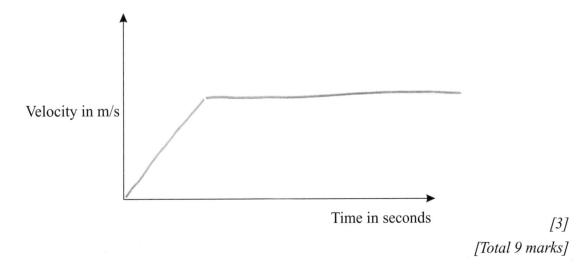

[3]

[Total 9 marks]

Section 1 — Forces and Motion

2   The diagram shows a velocity-time graph for a car during a section of a journey.

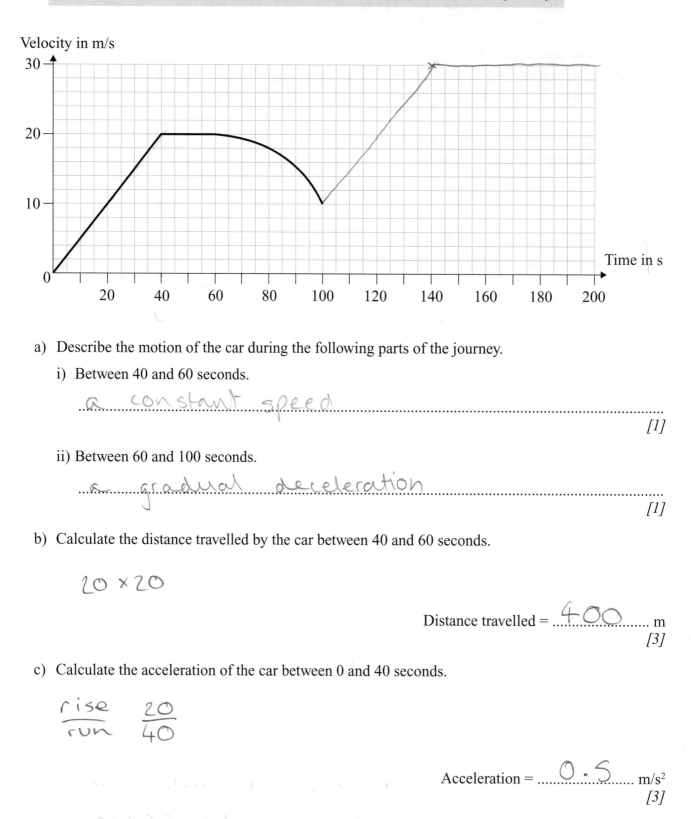

a) Describe the motion of the car during the following parts of the journey.

i) Between 40 and 60 seconds.

a constant speed

[1]

ii) Between 60 and 100 seconds.

a gradual deceleration

[1]

b) Calculate the distance travelled by the car between 40 and 60 seconds.

20 × 20

Distance travelled = 400 m

[3]

c) Calculate the acceleration of the car between 0 and 40 seconds.

$\frac{rise}{run}$ $\frac{20}{40}$

Acceleration = 0.5 m/s²

[3]

d) After 100 seconds, the car accelerates steadily for 40 seconds until it reaches a steady velocity of 30 m/s, which it maintains for 60 seconds. Complete the graph to show this motion.

[2]

[Total 10 marks]

Score:

19

Section 1 — Forces and Motion

Mass, Weight and Gravity

1 A student is measuring gravitational field strength, *g*, in a classroom experiment.
He takes an object with a mass of 2 kg and suspends it from a newton-meter held in his hand.
He takes multiple readings of the object's weight and calculates an average value of 19.6 N.

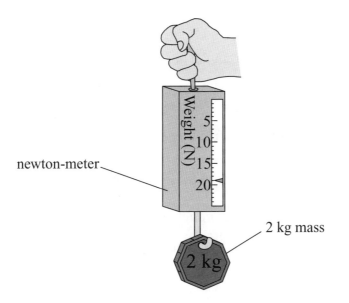

newton-meter

2 kg mass

2 kg

a) i) State the equation linking weight, mass and gravitational field strength.

weight = mass × gfs

[1]

ii) Calculate the gravitational field strength in the student's classroom and give the unit.

$g = \frac{w}{m}$ $\frac{19}{2} = 9.5$

Gravitational field strength = 9.5 .... unit N/kg ....
[3]

b) State how the student's measurement for the object's weight would differ if he performed the same experiment on the Moon. Explain your answer.

the object would have a smaller weight
as the gravitational field strength
would be weaker on the moon

[2]

[Total 6 marks]

Score:
6

Forces and Friction

1   There are a number of different forces that can cause an object to move.

   a) Give the name of the force that pulls objects towards the centre of Earth.

   .....gravity...

   [1]

   b) Complete the passage below using words from the box.

newtons	**watts**	**electrostatic**
potential	**frictional**	**pascals**

   When an object falls in air, it will experience a ....frictional.... force that opposes its

   motion. If two positively-charged objects are brought together, they will experience a repulsive

   ....electrostatic.... force. Both of these forces are measured in ....newtons........ .

   [3]

   [Total 4 marks]

2   The diagram below shows a truck moving forwards at a steady speed.
     The thrust (driving force) acting on the truck is shown.

Drag
Friction
thrust

   a) i) As the truck moves, it experiences resistance from drag and friction. Add an arrow to the
           diagram to show the direction in which the resistance acts, and label the arrow.

   [1]

   ii) Describe how the speed of the truck affects the resistance force it experiences.

   ....the higher the speed, the higher the....
   ....resistance.....

   [1]

   b) Draw and label an arrow to show **one** more force that acts on the truck.

   [2]

   [Total 4 marks]

   Score: [   ]

   8

Investigating Motion

1   A student investigates how high a tennis ball bounces
     after being dropped from different heights. She does
     this by dropping the ball from each height onto a
     hard surface next to a ruler. She reads and records
     the highest point reached by the ball after hitting the
     surface for the first time.

metre
rule → metre rule

tennis ball

hard surface

a) i) The table shows the student's results. Use the grid to plot
        a graph of bounce height against initial height using
        values from the table. Draw a line of best fit.

[5]

Initial height (cm)	20	30	40	50	60	70
Bounce height (cm)	13	21	12	35	41	49

    ii) Using the graph, describe the relationship between the initial height and the bounce height
        of the ball.

        ....

        ....

                                                                                                                    [1]

b) Describe how the student could alter the experiment to investigate how the height reached by the
    ball will change with each successive bounce.

    ....

    ....

    ....

                                                                                                                    [2]

                                                                                              [Total 8 marks]

                                                                                        Score:

                                                                                              8

Terminal Velocity

1   Dirk and Jenny are discussing the forces acting on an object falling at terminal velocity.

When an object is falling at terminal velocity, it is not accelerating because there are no forces acting on it.

When an object is falling at terminal velocity, the force of its weight is still pulling it down.

a)   State whose argument is **not** correct — Dirk or Jenny.

   ....

   Explain why.

   ....

   ....

   ....

   [2]

b)   Explain why a falling object reaches terminal velocity.

   ....

   ....

   ....

   [2]

c)   Dirk takes two balls of the same size but with different weights and drops them off a high balcony. Which of the two balls will have a lower terminal velocity? Explain your answer.

   ....

   ....

   ....

   ....

   [3]

   [Total 7 marks]

2 The students in a class are investigating how the area of an object's parachute affects the forces acting on it as it falls. They do this by attaching parachutes of varying sizes to a steel ball and dropping it from a fixed height, timing how long it takes to hit the ground.

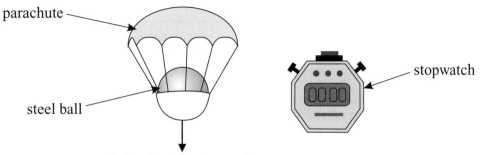

parachute

stopwatch

steel ball

weight of ball and parachute

a) i) Explain why using the same steel ball throughout the experiment will improve the validity of the result.

....

....

[2]

ii) Suggest and explain one other way in which the students can make sure the experiment is a valid test.

....

....

....

[2]

b) For each parachute, the steel ball initially accelerates before reaching terminal velocity. Complete the sentences using words from the box.

| larger | slowly | quickly | smaller |

i) The ball with the largest parachute will be travelling more .... than the other balls travelling at terminal velocity.

[1]

ii) The resistive forces due to air resistance are .... for larger parachutes.

[1]

c) Describe how the experiment could be altered to investigate how the mass of an object affects the forces acting on it as it falls.

....

....

[2]

[Total 8 marks]

Score: ☐

15

The Three Laws of Motion

1   Use words from the box to complete the passage below.

| unbalanced   stops   force   changing   accelerates   balanced |

The forces on a stationary object are always ...*balanced*... . If an object has a resultant

force acting on it, it ...*accelerates*... in the direction of the ...*force*... .

[Total 3 marks]

2   The table below shows the masses and maximum accelerations of four different antique cars.

Car	Mass (kg)	Maximum acceleration (m/s²)
Disraeli 9000	....	5
Palmerston 6i	1560	0.7
Heath TT	950	3
Asquith 380	790	2

a) Show that the Heath TT has a greater maximum driving force than the Asquith 380.

[3]

b) The Disraeli 9000 has a maximum driving force of 4000 N. Use this information to complete the
table above.

[1]
[Total 4 marks]

3   A camper van has a mass of 2500 kg. It is driven along a straight,
level road at a constant speed of 90 kilometres per hour.

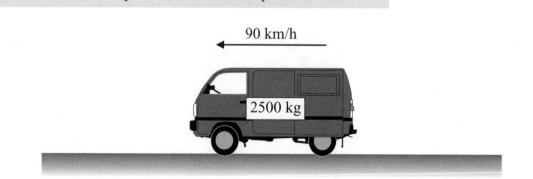

90 km/h

2500 kg

a) A headwind begins blowing with a force of 200 N, causing the van to slow down. Calculate the van's deceleration.

A headwind blows in the opposite direction to the van's motion.

Deceleration = ... m/s²

[3]

b) The van begins travelling at a steady speed before colliding with a stationary traffic cone with a mass of 10 kg. The traffic cone accelerates in the direction of the van's motion with an acceleration of 29 m/s².

i) Calculate the force applied to the traffic cone by the van.

Force = ... N

[2]

PAPER 2

ii) State the force applied by the cone to the van during the collision.

Remember Newton's third law of motion when you're answering this question.

Force = ... N

[1]

iii) Calculate the deceleration of the van during the collision.
Assume all of the force applied by the cone to the van causes the deceleration.

Deceleration = ... m/s²

[2]

[Total 8 marks]

4   Two students have fitted their scooters with the same engine. Student A and his scooter have a combined mass of 127.5 kg and a maximum acceleration of 2.40 m/s². Student B has a maximum acceleration of 1.70 m/s² on her scooter.

a) State the equation linking force, mass and acceleration.

....

[1]

b) Show that the combined mass of student B and her scooter is 180 kg.

The maximum force of the engine in each scooter = ... × .... = ... N

So, the mass of student B and her scooter =

[4]

[Total 5 marks]

Score: ☐

20

Combining Forces

1 Most quantities can be divided into two groups: scalars and vectors.

a) Describe the difference between a scalar and a vector quantity.

<u>scalar are a single unit and vectors have a direction</u>

[2]

b) Which of the following is a **vector**? Place a cross in the appropriate box to indicate your answer.

☐ speed ☐ distance ☒ mass ☒ force

[1]

c) Which of the following is a **scalar**? Place a cross in the appropriate box to indicate your answer.

☒ 14 kg ☐ 300 kN down ☐ 24 m/s west ☐ 1 m/s² up

[1]

[Total 4 marks]

2 Two jam jars are placed on a table. The forces acting on each jar are shown.

Jar A
10 N
10 N 17 N
10 N 3 N
2 N

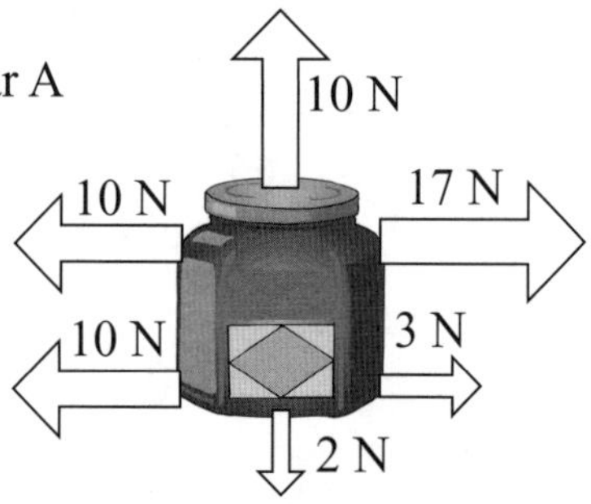

Jar B
y
x
5 N 20 N
4 N

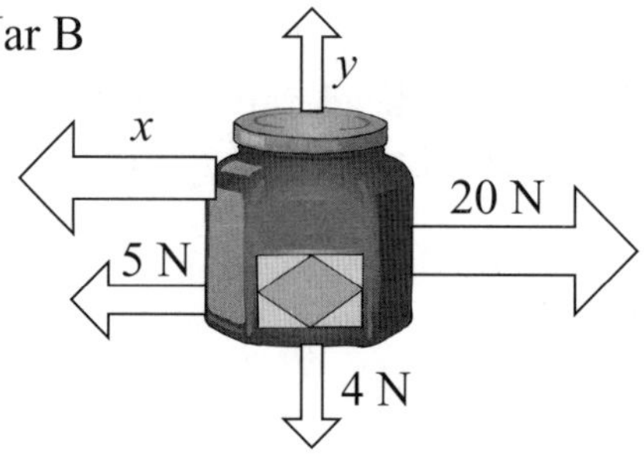

a) Calculate the resultant force acting on the jar A.

Force = ...8...... N   direction ...v.p......

[2]

b) The resultant force acting on jar B is zero.

i) Calculate the size of force y.

y = ...4..... N

[1]

ii) Calculate the size of force x.

x = ...15..... N

[1]

[Total 4 marks]

Score: ☐

8

Stopping Distances

1   The stopping distance of a car is the distance covered in the time between the driver first spotting a hazard and the car coming to a complete stop.

  a) i) What name is given to the distance travelled by a car between the driver first spotting a hazard and the driver applying the brakes?

  Thinking distance

  [1]

  ii) Give **two** factors that can affect this distance.

  Alchol, tierdness

  [2]

  b) i) What name is given to the distance travelled by a car between the brakes being applied and the car coming to a complete stop?

  braking distance

  [1]

  ii) Give **two** factors that can affect this distance.

  *weather, surface being driven on
  car speed*

  [2]

  [Total 6 marks]

2   Chloe is talking about how weather conditions can affect your stopping distance.

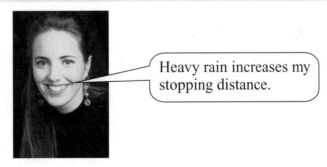

Heavy rain increases my stopping distance.

  a) State and explain **one** way in which heavy rain can increase a car's stopping distance.

  ○There is less friction on the road

  [2]

  b) Suggest **one** way Chloe could decrease her stopping distance if driving in heavy rain.

  drive slowly

  [1]

  [Total 3 marks]

Score:

9

Momentum and Collisions

1 A 1200 kg car is travelling at 30 m/s along the motorway. It crashes into the barrier of the central reservation and is stopped in a period of 1.2 seconds (after which its momentum is zero).

a) i) State the equation linking momentum, mass and velocity.

momentum = mass × velocity

[1]

ii) Calculate the momentum of the car before the crash and give the unit.

1200 × 30

Momentum = ...*36000*... unit ...*kg m/s*...

[3]

b) i) State the equation linking force, change in momentum and time taken.

force = change in momentum / time taken

[1]

ii) Calculate the size of the average force acting on the car during the collision.

$$\frac{30}{1.2} = 25$$

Force = ...*25*... N

[2]

[Total 7 marks]

2 A skater with a mass of 60 kg is moving at 5 m/s. He skates past a bag and picks it up from the floor, causing him to slow down to 4.8 m/s.

Calculate the mass of the bag. Assume there are no frictional forces.

initial momentum of skater = ...*60*... × ...*5*...

= ...*300*...

momentum of skater and bag = (...*60*... + mass$_{bag}$) × ...*4.8*...

Mass = ... kg

[Total 5 marks]

3 In a demolition derby, cars drive around an arena and crash into each other.

a) One car has a mass of 650 kg and a velocity of 15 m/s.
Calculate the momentum of the car and give the unit.

650×15

Momentum = ...9750.... unit ...Kg m/s...

[4]

b) The car collides head-first with another car with a mass of 750 kg. The two cars stick together.
Calculate the combined velocity of the two cars immediately after the collision if the other car
had a velocity of 10 m/s before the collision.

The cars collided head-first, so their velocities were in opposite directions before the crash — one will be negative

$9750 \longrightarrow \longleftarrow 7500$ 750×10

Velocity = ... m/s

[4]

c) The cars have crumple zones at the front of the car that crumple on impact.
Explain how a crumple zone reduces the forces acting on a driver during a collision.

The crumple zone increases time taken allowing the momentum and velocity to decrease for a smaller impact

[2]

[Total 10 marks]

Exam Practice Tip

Whenever you see a question about collisions there are two things of which you can be pretty sure — it's going to involve momentum and it's going to involve a lot of rearrangement. Similarly, if there's a question about car safety features, you can bet your lucky stars it'll be about changes in momentum over time.

Score

[ ]
___
22

Turning Forces and Centre of Gravity

1   A door has a horizontal door handle. To open the door, its handle needs to be rotated clockwise.

a) Pictures A, B, C and D show equal forces being exerted on the handle.

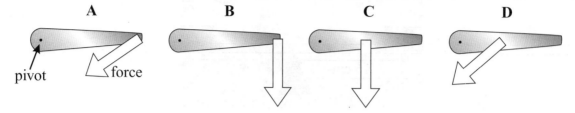

| A | B | C | D |

State which picture shows the largest moment on the handle. Explain your answer.

B, because the force is greater the futher away from the pivot that you go.

[2]

b) Complete the sentences below using words from the box.

| moment   gravity   balance   force   velocity |

i) The turning effect of a ....*force*.......... is called its moment.

[1]

ii) The weight of a body acts through its centre of ....*gravity*...... .

[1]

c) i) State the equation linking the moment, force and the perpendicular distance from the line of action of the force to the pivot.

.......*moment = force × distance from pivot*.......

[1]

ii) A force of 45 N is exerted vertically downwards on the door handle at a distance of 0.1 m from the pivot. Calculate the moment about the pivot and give the unit.

0.1 × 45

Moment = ...*4.5*...... unit ....*Nm*......

[3]

[Total 8 marks]

Principle of Moments

1   The diagram shows three weights on a wooden plank, resting on a pivot. Weight A is 2 N and
     sits 20 cm to the left of the pivot. Weight B exerts an anticlockwise moment of 0.8 Nm.
     Assume the plank has no weight.

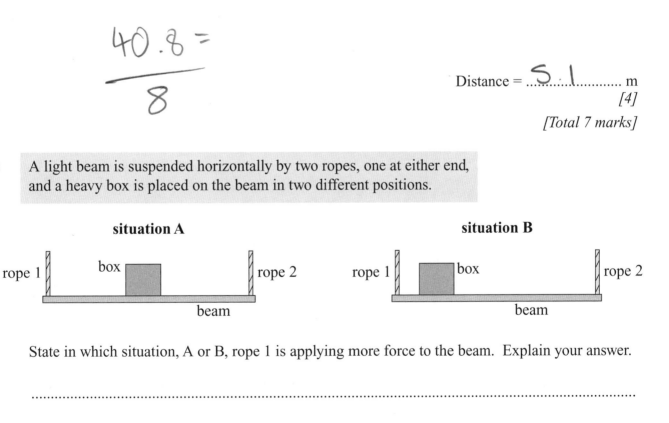

a)   Calculate the anticlockwise moment exerted by weight A.

20 × 2

Weight A anticlockwise moment = ...40........ Nm

[3]

b)   The system is currently balanced. Weight C has a weight of 8 N.
     Calculate the distance of weight C from the pivot.

$$\frac{40 \cdot 8 =}{8}$$

Distance = ...5.1.... m

[4]

[Total 7 marks]

2   A light beam is suspended horizontally by two ropes, one at either end,
     and a heavy box is placed on the beam in two different positions.

situation A   **situation B**

rope 1   box   rope 2   rope 1   box   rope 2
          beam   beam

     State in which situation, A or B, rope 1 is applying more force to the beam. Explain your answer.

     ....

     ....

     ....

[Total 2 marks]

Score:

9

Hooke's Law

1 A student wants to investigate how a type of rope extends when a force is applied to it.

a) The student suspends a piece of the rope vertically and hangs different weights from the rope. He measures the length of the rope before it has any weights attached with a mm ruler (read at eye level). He measures the length of the rope when each weight is attached to it by holding the ruler in the same place. He finds the extension of the rope for each weight by subtracting the original length of the rope from his length measurements.

Suggest **two** ways in which he could change his method to improve the validity of his results.

1. ....

....

2. ....

....

[2]

b) The student plots this graph of force against extension using the results from his experiment.

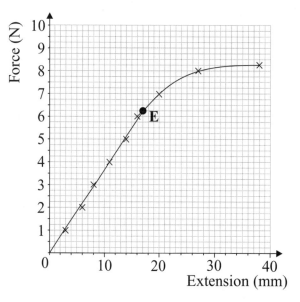

He writes a summary of his results. Use appropriate words to fill the blanks in the passage below.

Applying a force to the rope causes it to change .... Up to the point E

shown on the graph, the extension of the rope is directly .... to the applied

force, i.e. it obeys Hooke's law. In this region the rope also returns to its original shape

every time a weight is removed. This is known as .... behaviour.

[3]

[Total 5 marks]

Score:

5

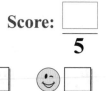

Gravity and the Universe

1　Place a cross in the appropriate box to indicate your answer.

a)　A galaxy is

☐ a star surrounded by orbiting planets.　　☐ a collection of billions of stars.　　☐ a collection of billions of universes.　　☐ a collection of 5 to 10 stars.

[1]

b)　Comets are lumps of icy rock which orbit

☐ the universe.　　☐ planets.　　☐ the galaxy.　　☐ the Sun.

[1]

c)　The universe contains

☐ billions of galaxies.　　☐ between 10 and 20 galaxies.　　☐ billions of other universes.　　☐ between 100 and 1000 galaxies.

[1]

[Total 3 marks]

2　Earth is part of the Solar System.

a)　State the name of the galaxy in which our solar system is found.

....

[1]

b)　Approximately what shape are the orbits of the planets in our solar system?

....

[1]

c)　Give the name used to describe any body that orbits planets such as Earth and the force that keeps them in orbit.

....

....

[2]

[Total 4 marks]

Score: ☐

7

Orbital Speed

1 These diagrams represent the orbits of four different objects in space.

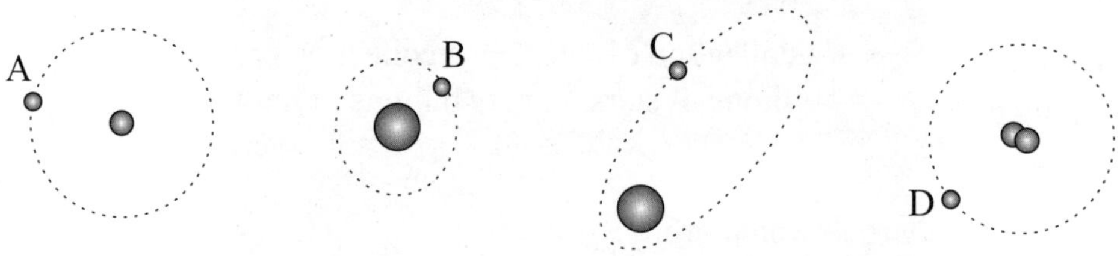

a) Which of the objects, A, B, C or D, is most likely to be a comet? Explain your answer.

....

....

[2]

b) Place a cross in the appropriate box to indicate your answer.

i) The orbits of moons are usually

☐ perfectly circular.   ☐ slightly elliptical.   ☐ highly elliptical.   ☐ helical.

[1]

ii) Comets usually have an orbital period that is

☐ the same as Earth's.   ☐ much shorter than Earth's.   ☐ much longer than Earth's.   ☐ a few days.

[1]

iii) Objects A and D have the same time period and orbital radius. Object D has an orbital speed of 1.2 km/s. What is the orbital speed of object A? Give a reason for your answer.

....

....

[1]

c) Object B has an orbital radius of 42 000 km and a time period of 1 day.
Calculate the orbital speed of object B and give the unit.

Orbital speed = ... unit ....

[3]

[Total 8 marks]

2   A comet orbits the Sun with a varying orbital radius and speed. It completes one orbit in precisely 72 years and its orbital speed is 48.1 km/s at the fastest point in its orbit.

a) Calculate the time period of the comet's orbit in seconds. Assume there are 365 days in a year.

Time period = ... s

[1]

b) At which point in the comet's orbit will its speed be **greatest**? Explain your answer.

....

....

....

[2]

c) Calculate the comet's distance from the centre of the Sun when it reaches the **fastest** point in its orbit.

Distance from the Sun = ... m

[3]

[Total 6 marks]

Score:

14

Section 2 — Electricity

Safe Plugs

1   The diagram shows some plug sockets and appliances in a kitchen.

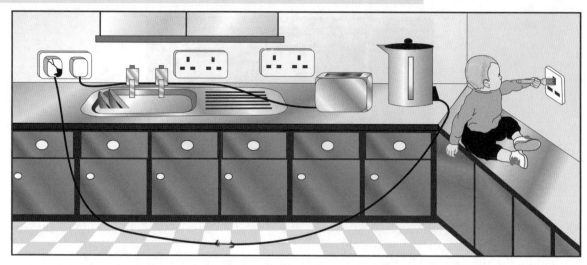

a) Give, with a reason, **two** ways that plugs are being used dangerously in this kitchen.

1. Frayed cable. Could expose Live wire ....

....

2. cracked casing. could expose Live ....

plug parts ....

[4]

b) i) The toaster in the diagram has a metal case and is wired with an earth wire for safety.
The kettle has a plastic case, and is not wired with an earth wire.
Explain why the kettle is still safe to use.

Plastic is not a conductive material

and therefore will not carry a charge

[2]

ii) A student claims "If no current is flowing in the toaster's earth wire, there must be a fault in
the toaster." Do you agree or disagree? Explain your answer.

Disagree when the toaster is working

there should be no charge through the

earth wire

[1]

c) Give **one** part of a plug that is made from copper or brass. Give a reason why this part is made
using one of these materials.

the wire these metals conduct

electricity very well

[2]

[Total 9 marks]

Score: ☐

9

Fuses and Circuit Breakers

1   A microwave oven has a metal casing.

a) i) An electrical fault develops in which the live wire comes into contact with the metal casing.
Explain why this can be dangerous.

This means that the casing will now be live ande expose any user to a shock
[1]

ii) The microwave oven is connected to a circuit breaker. Describe what happens to make the
microwave safe again when the fault in part i) occurs.

....

....

....

....
[3]

b) i) Some circuits are protected by fuses.
Describe the main difference between how a fuse and a circuit breaker work.

....

....
[2]

ii) Give **two** advantages of using circuit breakers instead of fuses to protect a circuit.

1. ....

....

2. ....

....
[2]

[Total 8 marks]

Score: ☐

8

Energy and Power in Circuits

1 The heating element in a kettle usually contains a coil of wire made of Nichrome. When the kettle is turned on, current flows through the coil of wire.

a) i) Explain why the coil of wire in the heating element is designed to have a high resistance.

so the wire does not break or melt due to high heat.

[1]

ii) Why does the current through the heating element decrease as it gets hotter?

As it gets hotter the resistance increases.

[1]

b) The table below shows the power and voltage ratings for two kettles.

	Power (kW)	Voltage (V)
Kettle A	2.8	230
Kettle B	3.0	230

i) State the equation linking power, voltage and current.

P = I V

[1]

ii) Calculate the current drawn from the mains supply by kettle A. State the correct unit.

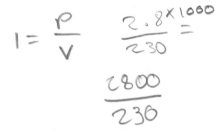

$$I = \frac{P}{V} \qquad \frac{2.8 \times 1000}{230} =$$

$$\frac{2800}{230}$$

Current = ...12.2.... unit ...A...

[3]

iii) What current rating should the fuse in kettle A have?
Place a cross in the appropriate box to indicate your answer.

☐ 1 A   ☐ 3 A   ☐ 5 A   ☑ 13 A

[1]

iv) A student is deciding whether to buy kettle A or kettle B. She wants to buy the kettle that boils water faster. Both kettles transfer 90% of the electrical energy supplied to the water. Suggest which kettle she should choose. Give a reason for your answer.

Kettle A as it has a bigger charge meaning the speed of energy transfer will be faster

[2]

[Total 9 marks]

2 A student is drilling holes to put up some shelves.
His electric drill is attached to a 12 V battery and uses a current of 2.3 A.

a) Drilling one hole transfers 828 J of electrical energy. Calculate the time taken to drill one hole.

$p = \frac{w}{~~A~~t}$

$\frac{w}{p} = t \qquad \frac{828}{12} =$

Time taken = ...69.... s
[3]

b) An electrical fault causes the fuse in the electric drill to blow. The student has the choice of replacing the blown fuse with a 1 A fuse or a 5 A fuse. The student says "I should use the 1 A fuse because it is closest to the operating current of the drill." Do you agree or disagree? Explain your answer.

Disagree the fuse must have a bigger A than the working A or it will blow as soon as you turn it on.
[2]
[Total 5 marks]

3 A student is comparing three lamps. Each lamp is connected in a separate circuit and she measures the current through it and the voltage across it. Her results are shown in the table below.

	Lamp A	Lamp B	Lamp C
Voltage (V)	12	3	230
Current (A)	2.5	4	0.1
Power (W)	30	12	....23....
Energy transferred in one minute (J)	1800	720	....

a) Complete the table by calculating and filling in the missing values.

[2]

b) State which lamp will transfer the most energy in one minute. ....
[1]
[Total 3 marks]

Exam Practice Tip

It's important that you can comfortably use $P = I \times V$ and $E = I \times V \times t$ to work out what fuse an appliance should be fitted with. The most common fuse ratings in the UK are 3 A, 5 A and 13 A and you should pick one just above the normal operating current to avoid it blowing for no reason, or not blowing at all.

Score
17

Circuits — the Basics

1   This question is about electric current.

a) Complete the passage below.

The voltage of the UK mains electrical supply is 230 .... The supply is an

.... current, which means that the direction of the current ....

[3]

b) Name the type of current supplied by cells and batteries.

....

[1]

[Total 4 marks]

2   A student wants to produce a graph of current against voltage for component X.
An incomplete diagram of the circuit he is going to use is shown below.

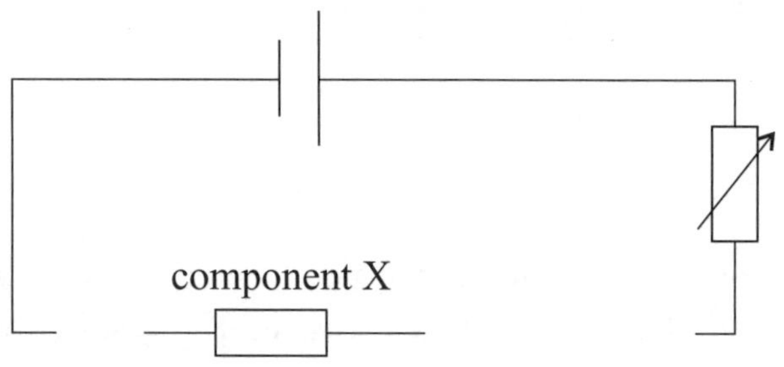

component X

a) Complete the circuit by adding an ammeter and a voltmeter.

[2]

b) The student increases the resistance of the variable resistor while keeping the voltage of the power
supply the same. Describe what will happen to the current in the circuit.

....

[1]

c) Describe a method the student could use to obtain a good set of data to produce his graph from.

....

....

....

....

....

[5]

[Total 8 marks]

Score:

12

Resistance and V = I × R

1 The diagram shows current-voltage (*I-V*) graphs for four components at a constant temperature.

a) Place a cross in the appropriate box to indicate your answer.
   All four components are types of

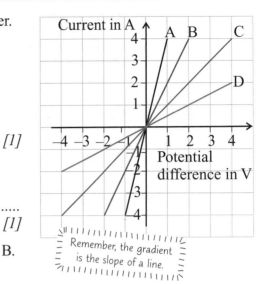

resistor	
filament lamp	
diode	

[1]

b) State which component has the highest resistance.

....

[1]

c) i) Calculate the gradient of the line graph for component B.

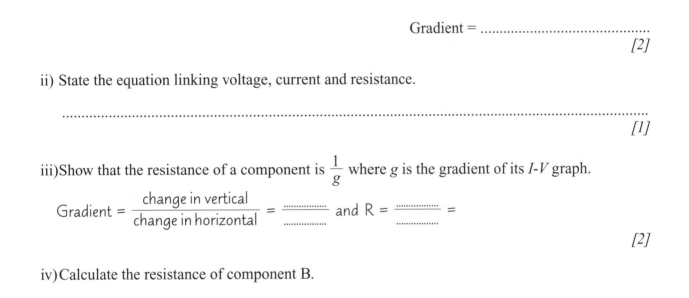

Gradient = ...

[2]

ii) State the equation linking voltage, current and resistance.

....

[1]

iii)Show that the resistance of a component is $\frac{1}{g}$ where *g* is the gradient of its *I-V* graph.

$\text{Gradient} = \dfrac{\text{change in vertical}}{\text{change in horizontal}} = \dfrac{............}{............}$ and $R = \dfrac{............}{............} =$

[2]

iv)Calculate the resistance of component B.

Resistance = ... Ω

[2]

v) The resistance of component B is tested at different temperatures. At 30 °C, it has a resistance of 0.75 Ω when the voltage across it is 15 V. Calculate the current through the component.

Current = ... A

[2]

[Total 11 marks]

Section 2 — Electricity

2   A student tries to identify two components using a standard test circuit.
     The table below shows his sets of readings of current and voltage for the two components.

Voltage (V)	−4.0	−3.0	−2.0	−1.0	0.0	1.0	2.0	3.0	4.0
Component A current (A)	0.0	0.0	0.0	0.0	0.0	0.2	1.0	2.0	4.5
Component B current (A)	−4.0	−3.5	−3.0	−2.0	0.0	2.0	3.0	3.5	4.0

a) Complete the student's conclusion:

"The table of data for component A suggests that it is a ....

because ...."

[2]

b) Draw a current-voltage (*I-V*) graph for component B on the graph paper. Draw a curve of best fit.

[5]

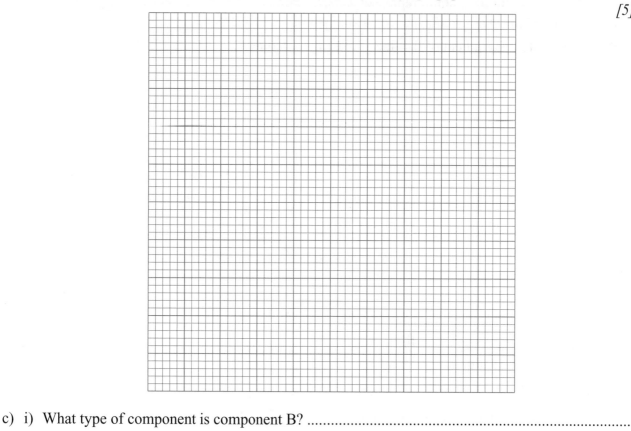

c) i) What type of component is component B? ....

[1]

ii) Explain the changes in the gradient of the *I-V* graph for component B between 0 V and 4 V.

....

....

....

[3]

[Total 11 marks]

LDRs, Thermistors and LEDs

1   This question is about circuit components.

a)   Place a cross in the appropriate box to indicate your answer to each question.

i)   Which circuit symbol below represents a fuse?

☐ ─▭⁄─   ☐ ─▢▢─   ☐ ─▭─   ☐ ─▭⁄─   *[1]*

ii)   Which circuit symbol below does **not** represent a type of power source?

☐ ─o o─   ☐ ─o∿o─   ☐ ─┤├┄┤├─   ☐ ─o o─   *[1]*

b)   i)   Draw a circuit diagram to represent a circuit in which the brightness of a lamp depends on temperature. The circuit should contain **three** components.

[3]

ii)   Describe and explain how the circuit current changes as the room temperature increases.

....

....
[2]

[Total 7 marks]

2   The diagram below shows a circuit that contains an LED, a light-dependent resistor and a cell.

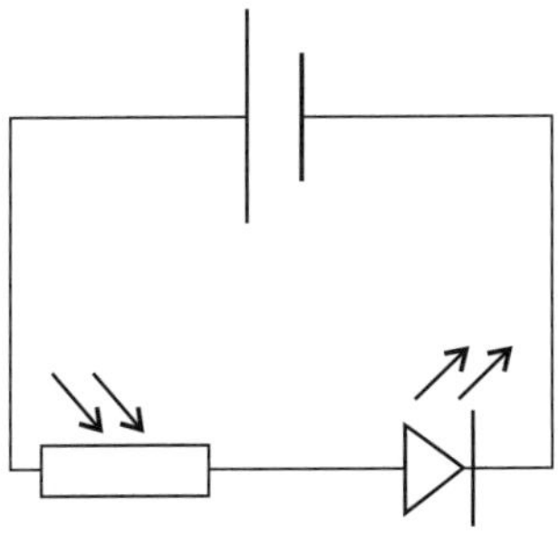

a)   Describe how you could tell that a current is flowing in the circuit.

....
[1]

b)   Thermistors are another type of resistor.

i)   Give **one** similarity of thermistors and light-dependent resistors.

....
[1]

ii)   Give **one** difference between thermistors and light-dependent resistors.

....
[1]

[Total 3 marks]

Score: ☐

10

Series and Parallel Circuits

1   14 fairy light bulbs are wired in series with a 12 V battery.

a) i) Give **one** advantage of wiring the fairy lights in parallel instead. ....

....

[1]

ii) The current through one of the bulbs is 0.5 A. Calculate the total resistance in the circuit.

Resistance = ... Ω

[3]

iii) Describe how the current in the circuit would change if there were only 9 bulbs in series connected to the same battery.

....

[1]

b) A student makes the following observation.

The windscreen wipers, headlights and air conditioning can all be turned on and off separately in my parents' car.

Explain her observation.

....

....

[1]

[Total 6 marks]

Score:

6

Charge, Voltage and Energy Change

1   A 3 volt battery can supply a current of 5 amps for 20 minutes before it needs recharging.

a) i) State what is meant by **current**.

....
[1]

   ii) How does current flow through metal wires in a circuit?

....
[1]

b) i) State the equation that links charge, current and time.

....
[1]

   ii) Calculate how much charge will pass through the circuit before the battery needs recharging.
       State the correct unit.

Charge = ... unit ....
[4]

   iii) A student recharges the battery and uses it again. This time it discharges in half the original
        time, but the same amount of charge passes through the circuit in that time. State how this will
        affect the current that the battery supplies over this time.

....
[1]

PAPER 2

c) State, with a reason, how much energy is transferred by the battery per coulomb of charge passed
    through the circuit. State the correct unit.

....

....

....
[3]
[Total 11 marks]

Score:

11

Static Electricity

1 This question is about the electrical properties of different materials.

a) State what is meant by an electrical insulator.

....

[1]

b) Complete the table below.

[2]

Material	Electrical conductor?	Electrical insulator?
Glass	No	Yes
Water	Yes	No
Plastic	....	....
Copper	....	....

[Total 3 marks]

PAPER 2

2 A student does some experiments to study static electricity. He uses a cloth duster to rub a rubber balloon. The balloon gains an electrostatic charge.

a) Explain, in terms of charge movement, how the balloon becomes positively charged.

....

....

[2]

b) Describe an experiment that could be used to show that the balloon has an electrostatic charge.

....

....

....

[2]

c) The balloon has a charge of 1.5 μC. What charge does the cloth used to rub it have? Give a reason for your answer.

....

....

[2]

[Total 6 marks]

PAPER 2

3 A Van de Graaff generator is a machine which is used to generate static electricity. A student uses one type of Van de Graaff generator in class and writes the following description of how it works.

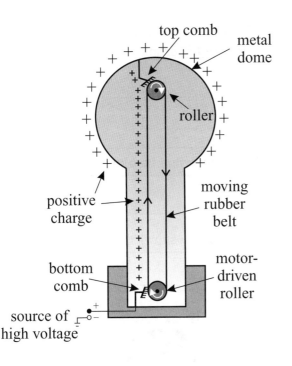

top comb
metal dome
roller
positive charge
moving rubber belt
bottom comb
motor-driven roller
source of high voltage

- The bottom comb is positively charged and attracts electrons away from the rubber belt.

- The rubber belt loses electrons and becomes positively charged.

- As the positive charge on the belt passes the top comb, electrons are attracted from the metal dome onto the belt.

- The metal dome loses electrons and builds up a positive static charge.

a) Explain why the belt is made from rubber.

....

....

[2]

b) Explain why the top comb needs to be made from a conductor.

....

[1]

c) Explain why electrons are attracted from the metal dome to the belt.

....

[1]

d) Tiny pieces of paper are scattered onto the dome of the Van de Graaff generator. The pieces of paper appear to 'jump' off the dome as soon as they touch the surface. Suggest why this happens.

....

....

....

[2]

[Total 6 marks]

Score:

15

Static Electricity — Examples

1 A student prints a document from a computer using an inkjet printer.

a) An inkjet printer works by firing charged droplets of ink towards a piece of paper. Explain how the printer can control and alter the direction of the droplets of ink.

....

....

....

....

[3]

b) The student then photocopies the document. The diagram below shows the main steps that a photocopier uses to make a paper copy of a document.

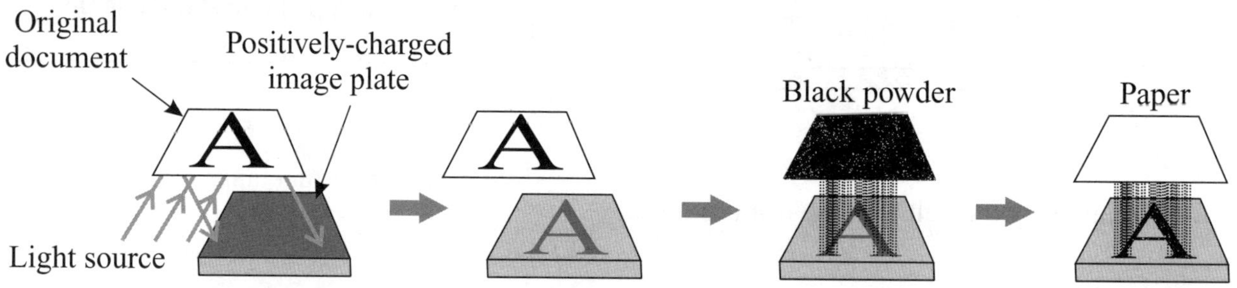

Original document   Positively-charged image plate

Black powder   Paper

Light source

Light is reflected off the original document onto the image plate.

Some of the image plate loses its charge.

Black powder transferred to image plate.

Powder transferred to paper.

i) Before the process starts, the image plate is positively charged. Describe what causes some parts of the image plate to lose their charge.

....

....

[1]

ii) Describe how the original image is transferred to the paper after the light source has been reflected off it.

Think about what's attracted to what throughout the process.

The black parts of the document don't reflect light onto the plate, so

the image plate keeps...

....

....

....

....

[5]

[Total 9 marks]

2   A tall building is fitted with a lightning rod, made from a conductor, that safely directs charge to earth when the building is struck by lightning. Explain how lightning is caused.

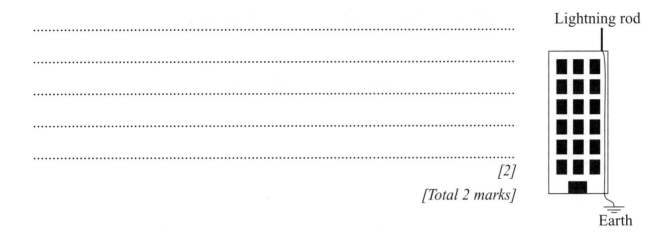

Lightning rod

....

....

....

....

....

[2]

[Total 2 marks]

Earth

3   When refuelling a vehicle, fuel flows out of a fuel nozzle and into the vehicle's fuel tank.

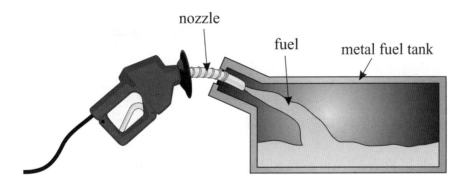

nozzle   fuel   metal fuel tank

a)   Explain why it is dangerous if static charge is allowed to build up during this process.

....

....

[2]

b)   Give **two** safety measures that can be taken to reduce the build-up of static charge when fuelling.

1. ....

....

2. ....

....

[2]

[Total 4 marks]

Score:

15

Section 3 — Waves
Waves — The Basics

1   Waves can be either transverse or longitudinal.

   a)   Complete the sentence using words from the box.

> matter   frequency   energy   wavelength   information   amplitude

     Waves transfer .... and ....

     without transferring any ....

                                                      [3]

   b)   A student uses a spring to produce the two types of waves shown — type A and type B.

                        type A   type B

     i)   State, with a reason, whether type B is transverse or longitudinal.

       ....

                                                      [1]

     ii)   Describe how type A waves and type B waves are different in terms of the direction of their vibrations.

       ....

       ....

                                                      [2]

   c)   Give **one** example of a type A wave other than a wave on a spring.

       ....

                                                      [1]

                                                 [Total 7 marks]

2   A wave in a pond, travelling at 0.5 m/s, makes a floating ball move up and down twice every second.

                       ←   wave speed 0.5 m/s

   a)   What is the frequency of the wave? State the correct unit.

                                        Frequency = ... unit ....

                                                      [2]

   b)   i)   State the equation linking wave speed, frequency and wavelength.

       ....

                                                      [1]

     ii)   The ball is on a crest of the wave. Calculate how far away the next crest is from the ball.

                                              Distance = ... m

                                                      [2]

iii)Calculate the time period of the wave.

Time period = ... s

[2]

[Total 7 marks]

3   The diagram shows three electromagnetic waves, A, B and C.

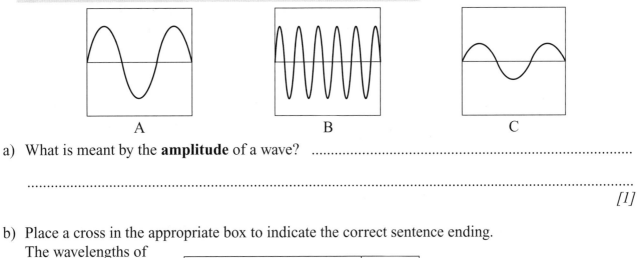

A   B   C

a) What is meant by the **amplitude** of a wave? ....

....

[1]

b) Place a cross in the appropriate box to indicate the correct sentence ending.
The wavelengths of

[1]

A and B are the same.	
A and C are the same.	
B and C are the same.	

c) A student uses a ripple tank to produce a water wave. He measures an amplitude of 1 cm and a wavelength of 2 cm and draws a graph of the wave, as shown in the diagram.

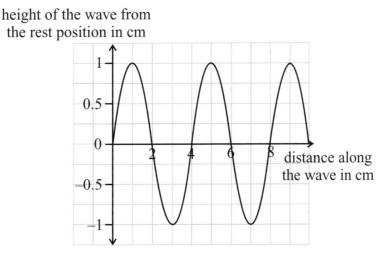

height of the wave from
the rest position in cm

distance along
the wave in cm

i) Which property of the wave has the student drawn incorrectly? Explain your answer.

....

[1]

ii) On the same set of axes, sketch a wave with a wavelength of 6 cm and an amplitude of 0.75 cm.

[2]

[Total 5 marks]

Score:

19

Wave Behaviour and EM Waves

1 Some satellite signals are microwaves. They are received by a satellite dish like the one shown.

dish

detector

a) The microwaves bounce off the white dish onto the small circular detector in the middle. Name the process of waves bouncing back when they meet a surface.

....

[1]

b) Complete the sentence below.

Think about the order of the electromagnetic spectrum.

High frequency microwave radiation is closest in

frequency to low frequency .... radiation.

[1]

c) State, with a reason, whether satellite signals travel faster in free space than radio signals.

....

[1]

PAPER 2

[Total 3 marks]

2 All types of waves can undergo diffraction.

a) Describe what is meant by **diffraction**. ....

....

[1]

b) i) The range of wavelengths of visible light is around 400-700 nm. Explain why visible light does not appear to diffract when it passes through doorways.

'nm' means nanometres, or 1×10^{-9} m.

....

....

....

[2]

ii) A student claims: "Radio waves are a type of electromagnetic wave, just like visible light. This means you won't be able to detect radio waves diffracting as they pass through doorways either." Do you agree or disagree? Explain your answer.

....

....

....

[2]

[Total 5 marks]

Score:

8

Uses of Electromagnetic Waves

1   Electromagnetic waves have many practical uses.

a) Place a cross in the appropriate box to indicate your answer to each question part.

   i) Gamma rays are used in

   ☐ the sterilisation of medical equipment.   ☐ satellite communications.   ☐ photography.   ☐ the imaging of bones.

   [1]

   ii) In some ovens, food is heated as a result of water molecules in the food absorbing

   ☐ gamma rays.   ☐ microwaves.   ☐ radio waves.   ☐ X-rays.

   [1]

   iii)Short-wave radio signals can be received at long distances from the transmitter because they

   ☐ reflect off the ionosphere.   ☐ bend round the curvature of the Earth.

   ☐ travel easily through Earth's crust.   ☐ bend round hills and obstacles.

   [1]

b) Complete the passage below using some of the words from the box.

data	protons	reflect	diffract	electrons

   .... can be transmitted very long distances using optical fibres. Signals

   are sent as pulses of light that .... along the core of the optical fibre.   *[2]*

   [Total 5 marks]

2   Infrared cameras can show how much heat something is giving out by detecting the infrared radiation coming from it. The diagram shows a visible light photograph and an infrared photograph of the same person, taken one after the other.

visible light photograph   infrared photograph

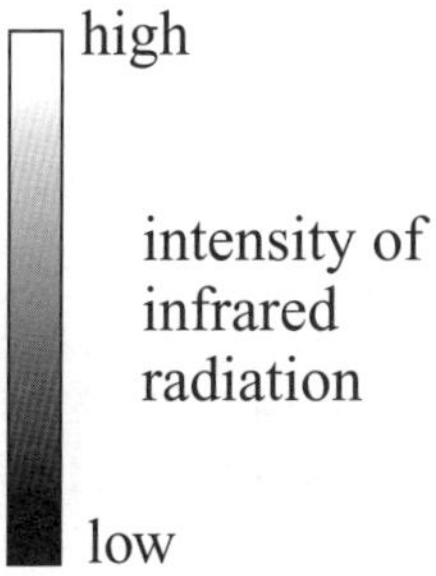

high

intensity of infrared radiation

low

a) Which part of the person is giving out the most heat? Explain how you know.

   ....

   ....

   ....

   [3]

b) Give **one** use of infrared imaging.

   ....

   [1]

c) Give **one** device designed to produce infrared radiation. Explain why it does this.

....

....

[2]

[Total 6 marks]

3 The radio transmitter shown transmits long-wave radio signals as well as short-wave TV signals. A mountain blocks the line of sight between the transmitter and a house, as shown.

radio transmitter

a) Explain why the mountain does not stop long-wave radio signals from reaching the house.

....

....

[2]

b) Describe how short-wave TV signals from the transmitter reach the house.

....

[1]

c) The home owner decides to get satellite TV installed.

i) State what type of electromagnetic radiation is used to send signals to satellites.

....

[1]

ii) Describe how satellite TV signals are transmitted from a transmitter on the ground to the house.

....

....

[2]

[Total 6 marks]

4 The diagram shows electromagnetic radiation being used to sterilise a surgical instrument.

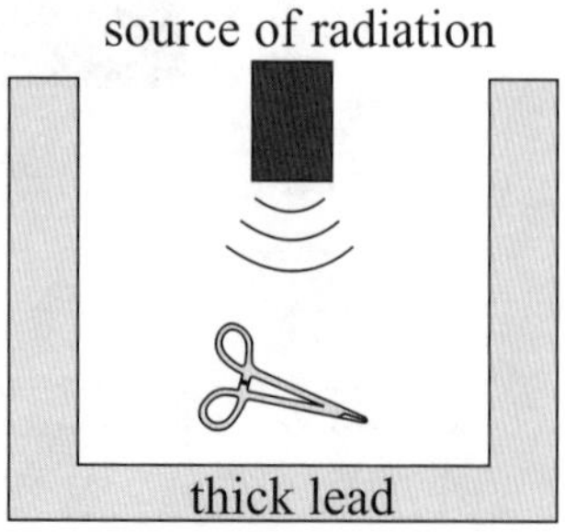

source of radiation

a) State what type of electromagnetic radiation is being used.

....

[1]

b) A similar process can be used to treat fruit before it is exported to other countries. Suggest why this process is used.

thick lead

....

....

[2]

[Total 3 marks]

5 Ultraviolet radiation can damage skin cells and cause cancer in humans.

a) A student claims "Fluorescent lamps are harmful to humans because they emit ultraviolet radiation." Do you agree or disagree? Explain your answer.

....

....

....

[2]

b) Photographers sometimes use ultraviolet filters to prevent ultraviolet radiation from reaching the camera's sensor or film. Describe how a camera creates a photograph using visible light, and how the camera and the photographer can control the amount of visible light entering it.

....

....

....

....

[3]

[Total 5 marks]

6 X-rays are used by truck scanners at country border control points.

a) Complete the passage below using words from the box.

absorbed	heat	contents	produced	outside

X-rays sent through a truck are .... different amounts by different objects

inside the truck. An X-ray detector is used to measure how much X-ray radiation passes through

the truck. It creates an image of the .... of the truck.

[2]

b) During a scan, the driver and any passengers are asked to step outside of the vehicle for their safety. Suggest why this happens.

....

....

....

[2]

[Total 4 marks]

Score:

29

Dangers of Electromagnetic Waves

1 Mobile phones use microwaves to transmit signals.

a) Suggest why people might be worried that excessive mobile phone use could be harmful.

....

....

[1]

b) Explain why it would be more dangerous to use infrared radiation instead of microwaves for mobile phone signals.

....

....

[2]

[Total 3 marks]

2 Sunlight contains ultraviolet radiation.

a) Explain why excessive sunbathing can be dangerous.

....

....

[2]

b) Describe **one** method of protecting yourself from the sun.

....

....

[1]

[Total 3 marks]

3 Living cells in the human body can absorb gamma rays.

a) Give **two** damaging effects that gamma rays can have when they are absorbed by living cells.

1. ....

2. ....

[2]

b) Gamma radiation can be used to treat cancer by killing the cancerous cells. Give **one** precaution that should be taken when giving a cancer patient a dose of gamma radiation.

....

[1]

[Total 3 marks]

Score: ☐

9

☹ ☐   😐 ☐   🙂 ☐

Reflection of Waves

1 A student looks in the mirror at himself and sees an image formed from reflected light.

a) i) State what is meant by the **normal** of a ray of light hitting a surface.

....

....

[1]

ii) State the law of reflection.

....

....

[1]

b) i) On the diagram, draw the paths of **two** rays of light to show how the student sees an image in the plane mirror of point A.

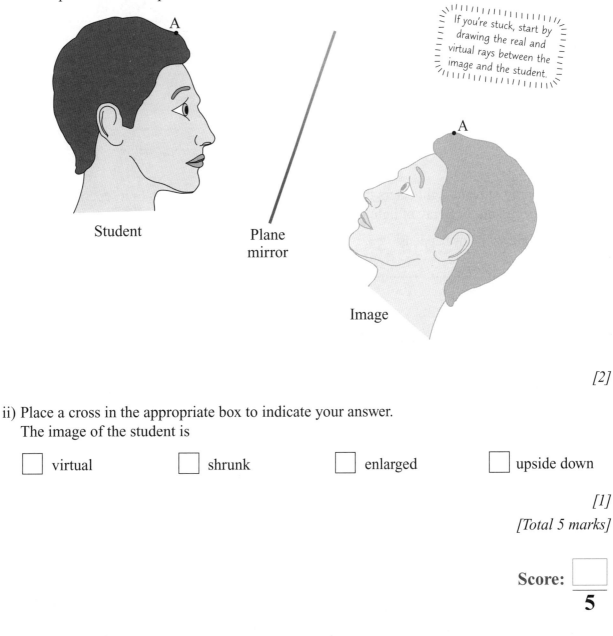

If you're stuck, start by drawing the real and virtual rays between the image and the student.

Student

Plane mirror

A

Image

[2]

ii) Place a cross in the appropriate box to indicate your answer.
The image of the student is

☐ virtual   ☐ shrunk   ☐ enlarged   ☐ upside down

[1]

[Total 5 marks]

Score: ☐

5

☹ ☐   😐 ☐   🙂 ☐

Section 3 — Waves

Refraction of Waves

1   The diagram shows a ray of red light entering a glass prism.

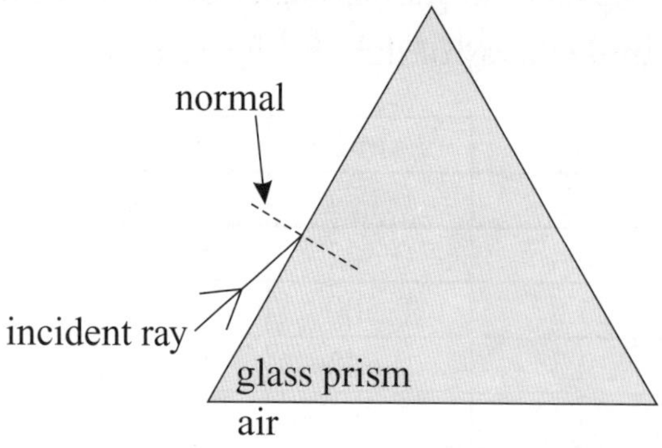

normal

incident ray

glass prism

air

a) Complete the diagram to show the ray passing through the prism and emerging from the other side. Label the angles of incidence, *i*, and refraction, *r*, for both boundaries.

[3]

b) Describe an experiment that you could do to measure *i* and *r* at both boundaries.

....

....

....

....

....

[4]

c) When a ray of white light enters the prism, several rays of light, each of a separate colour, emerge from the prism. Each ray of light travels in a slightly different direction.

i) Explain why this happens.

....

....

....

[2]

ii) When white light shines through a rectangular block of glass instead of through a triangular prism, all the light that emerges travels in the same direction. Explain why.

....

....

....

[2]

[Total 11 marks]

Score:

11

Refractive Index and Snell's Law

1 A student is investigating the refractive index of a block of transparent material. She shines a ray of yellow light at the block at various angles of incidence (i) and measures the angles of refraction (r). The table shows her results.

i	r	sin i	sin r
10.0°	8.3°	0.174	0.144
20.0°	16.4°	0.342	0.282
30.0°	24.8°	0.500	0.419
40.0°	32.3°	0.643	0.534
50.0°	39.8°	0.766	0.640
60.0°	46.2°	0.866	0.722

a) Use the values in the table to draw a graph of sin r against sin i.

[5]

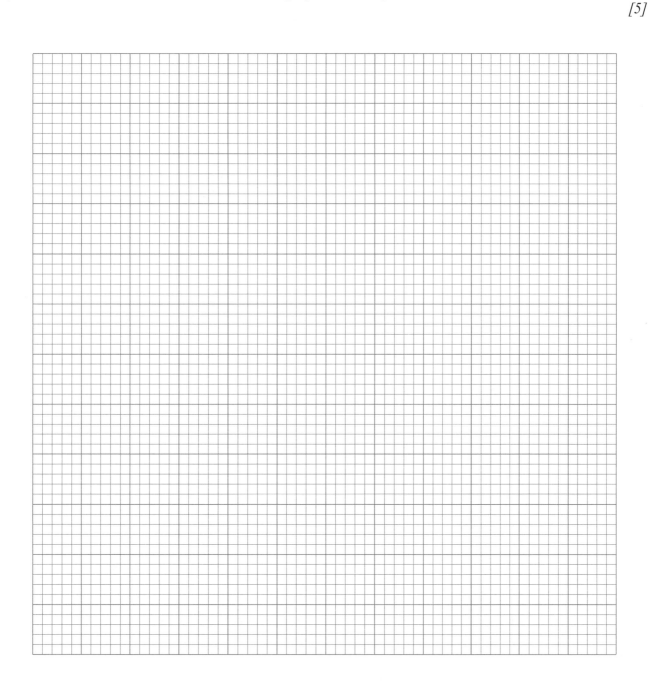

b) Use your graph to calculate the refractive index of the material for yellow light.

Refractive index = ...

[4]

[Total 9 marks]

2 The diagram shows white light refracting at an air-glass boundary and separating into colours.

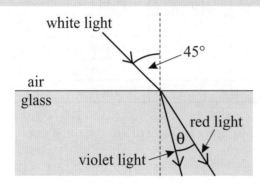

a) The refractive index of glass for red light is 1.514. Calculate the angle of refraction for red light.

Angle of refraction = ...°

[4]

b) Explain why the ray of white light would not separate into colours if it crossed the boundary along the normal.

....

....

[2]

c) The refractive index of glass for violet light is 1.528. Calculate the angle θ shown in the diagram.

Angle of incidence for violet light = i = ...

$\sin r = \dfrac{\sin i}{n}$ (where r is the angle of refraction for violet light and n is the refractive index for violet light of the glass block).

$= \dfrac{\sin ....}{1.528} = $ .... $\Rightarrow r = $ ....

$\theta = $ .... $-$ ....

$= $ ....

$\theta = $ ....°

[4]

[Total 10 marks]

Score: ☐

19

Refractive Index and Critical Angles

1 Endoscopes use optical fibres to look inside a patient's body. When light meets the boundary between the optical fibre core and the outer cladding, there is total internal reflection.

a) State what is meant by **total internal reflection**.

....

....

[1]

b) Explain why bending the endoscope too sharply may result in reduced image quality.

Think about how the angle of incidence will change.

....

....

[2]

[Total 3 marks]

2 Light passes through the acrylic bottom of a boat into the water below it. The critical angle (C) of the acrylic-water boundary for the light is 63.2°.

a) State what is meant by the **critical angle** for a boundary.

....

[1]

b) What can you say about the angle of incidence of a ray of light that passes through the boundary between the acrylic and the water?

....

[1]

c) Another ray of light meets the acrylic-water boundary at an angle of incidence of 70°. Describe what will happen to the ray of light at the boundary.

....

[1]

d) The diagram shows a ray of light hitting the boundary between the same acrylic and air. Calculate the refractive index of the acrylic.

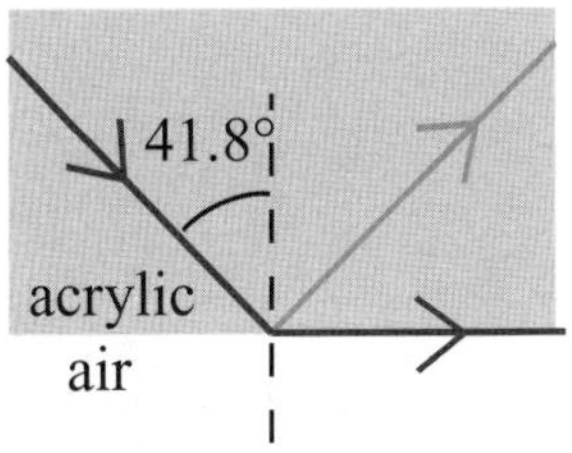

Refractive index = ...

[3]

[Total 6 marks]

Exam Practice Tip

Don't forget, total internal reflection only happens when light is going from a material with a higher refractive index to a material with a lower refractive index. The cladding of an optical fibre must have a lower refractive index than the core, otherwise the light will always escape, no matter how large the angle of incidence.

Score / **9**

Analogue and Digital Signals

1 The diagram below shows how the surface of a CD and a vinyl record differ and how they are read. A CD player shines a laser at the CD's surface and detects whether it is shining at a pit or onto a bump. A record player uses a needle to trace the surface of the record up and down.

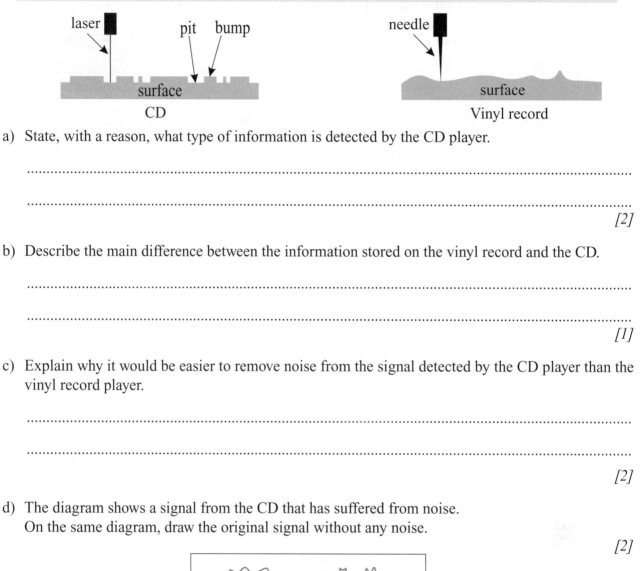

a) State, with a reason, what type of information is detected by the CD player.

....

....

[2]

b) Describe the main difference between the information stored on the vinyl record and the CD.

....

....

[1]

c) Explain why it would be easier to remove noise from the signal detected by the CD player than the vinyl record player.

....

....

[2]

d) The diagram shows a signal from the CD that has suffered from noise.
On the same diagram, draw the original signal without any noise.

[2]

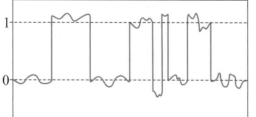

e) The CD player is also a digital radio player. Give **one** advantage of transmitting digital radio signals compared to analogue radio signals.

....

....

[1]

[Total 8 marks]

Score:

8

Sound Waves

1   The diagram shows how an oscilloscope can be used to display sound waves by connecting microphones to it. Trace 1 shows the sound waves detected by microphone 1 and trace 2 shows the sound waves detected by microphone 2.

a) i) A student uses the equipment. He begins with both microphones at equal distances from the speaker and the signal generator set at a fixed frequency. He gradually moves microphone 2 away from the speaker, which causes the trace shown for microphone 2 to move. He stops moving microphone 2 when the traces for both microphones line up again as shown in the diagram. He measures the distance the microphone has moved.

Explain how his measurement could be used to work out the speed of sound.

......using the equation s=d/t so you could work out how long it takes to go from one microphone to the other [2]

ii) With the signal generator set to 50 Hz, the distance between the microphones was measured to be 6.8 m. Calculate the speed of sound in air. State the correct unit.

Speed = ... unit ....

[4]

PAPER 2

b) One microphone is removed and the signal generator is adjusted. The diagram shows the trace produced on the oscilloscope.

i) Place a cross in the appropriate box to indicate your answer to this question.
Quantity X marked on the trace represents the

☐ wavelength   ☐ frequency

☐ amplitude   ☑ time period

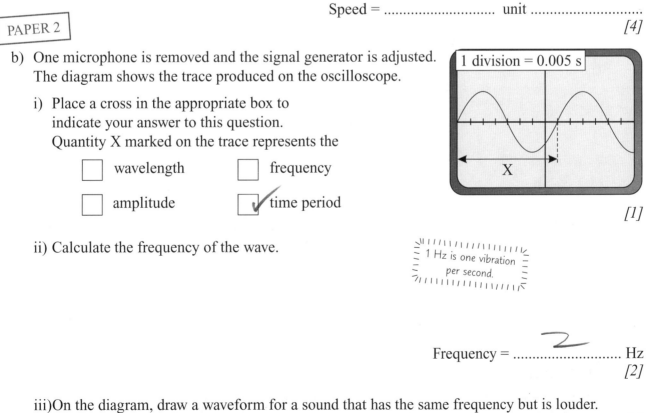

[1]

ii) Calculate the frequency of the wave.

1 Hz is one vibration per second.

Frequency = ...2............ Hz

[2]

iii) On the diagram, draw a waveform for a sound that has the same frequency but is louder.

[1]

[Total 10 marks]

2   A student sings in her school choir. She practises in both an empty drama hall and on the school playing field. She notices that her voice echoes only when she sings in the drama hall.

a) Explain why her voice echoes in the drama hall but not on the playing field.

....

....
[1]

b) Some of the sound produced by the student passes through the walls of the hall.
As it does this, its speed increases and its wavelength increases.

Suggest **one** other way the sound may change as it passes through the hall walls.

....
[1]

c) Another student joins in the practice.
The sound waves he produces have a much lower frequency.

i) State the range of frequencies a student with good hearing should be able to hear.

....
[1]

PAPER 2

ii) How does the pitch of the male student's voice differ from that of the female student's?
Explain your answer.

....

....
[2]

PAPER 2

d) The drama hall is fitted with sound insulation so that sound
can no longer pass through the walls and windows.

friend →●

drama hall

↗
door

●← student

A friend notices that if the door is open, she can still hear the student singing from round the
corner even though she can't see her. Explain why.

....
[1]

[Total 6 marks]

Exam Practice Tip	**Score**
Describing an experiment to measure the speed of sound could bag you loads of marks. To get top marks, you'll need to be really familiar with all the details, including what you'll measure, what you'll use to measure it with, the formulas you'll need to use and an idea of some realistic values for which the experiment will work.	**16**

Conservation of Energy

1 This question is about energy transfers.

Complete the table below showing the energy input and useful energy output for various devices.

Device	Energy input	Useful energy output
A spring-loaded catapult	....	kinetic energy
A portable radio	chemical energy	....
....	electrical energy	heat energy

[Total 3 marks]

2 A light bulb transfers electrical energy into 20 J of light energy and 80 J of heat energy every second. You may assume that these are the only energy transfers.

a) Complete the passage below using words from the box.

stored	**transferred**	**absorbed**	**created**	**reflected**

Energy can be .... usefully from one form to another, but it can

never be .... or destroyed.

[2]

b) How much electrical energy is supplied to the bulb each second? Explain your answer.

....

....

[2]

[Total 4 marks]

Score

7

Efficiency

1   Torch A transfers 20 J of chemical energy per second. It emits 8 J of light
     energy, 11.5 J of heat energy and 0.5 J of sound energy every second.

a) Name the useful output energy of torch A.

     ....
                                                                                        [1]

b) i) State the equation linking efficiency, useful energy output and total energy input.

        ....
                                                                                        [1]

    ii) Calculate the efficiency of torch A.

    The input energy is
    the total amount of
    energy transferred.

                                                            Efficiency = ...
                                                                                        [2]

c) Torch B has an efficiency of 0.55 and emits 10 J of useful light energy each second.
    Calculate how much energy is supplied to the torch per second.

                                        Energy supplied per second = ... J
                                                                                        [2]

d) Each torch is powered by an identical battery. A student claims that the battery in torch B will
    go 'flat' quicker than in torch A because it emits more light energy. Do you agree or disagree?
    Explain your answer.

     ....

     ....
                                                                                        [1]
                                                                                [Total 7 marks]

                                                                        Score: ☐
                                                                                  ———
                                                                                    7

Energy Transfers

1   A nuclear power station generates electricity using nuclear reactions.

a) Which of the following shows the useful energy transfer in a nuclear reactor?
Place a cross in the appropriate box to indicate your answer.

☐ nuclear → heat   ☐ electrical → heat   ☐ electrical → nuclear   ☐ heat → nuclear

[1]

b) A television is powered using electricity from the power station. Describe **one** energy transfer
that occurs in a television. State whether this is a useful energy transfer or not a useful transfer.

....

[2]

[Total 3 marks]

2   A weight lifter is holding a set of weights still above his head.

a) Name the type of energy the set of weights has.

....

[1]

b) Describe the energy transfers involved when the weight lifter raises the weights.

....

....

[2]

c) The weight lifter drops the weights. Describe the energy transfer that will take place as they fall
towards the floor.

....

[1]

[Total 4 marks]

Score: ☐
─────
7

☹ ☐   ☺ ☐   ☺ ☐

Sankey Diagrams

1   The manufacturer of a toy crane creates a Sankey diagram to show
    the energy transfers involved when the crane is in operation.

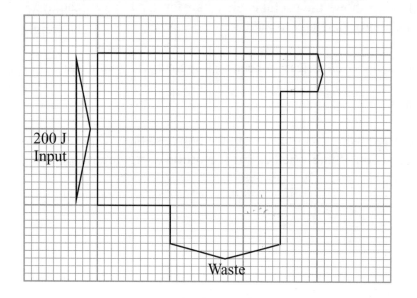

a) Calculate the value represented by each small square.

                                        1 square = ...10........... J

                                                            [1]

b) Calculate how much energy is transferred usefully by the toy crane for every 200 J
    of energy supplied.

                                Useful energy transferred = ...60.......... J

                                                            [1]

c) Four fifths of the energy wasted is wasted as heat energy and one fifth as sound.
    Use the grid below to draw a Sankey diagram for the crane to show this information.

                                                            [3]

                                                    [Total 5 marks]

2   A winch uses a cable and a hook to lift a weight by winding the cable around a drum.
     Below is a Sankey diagram for the winch lifting a weight.

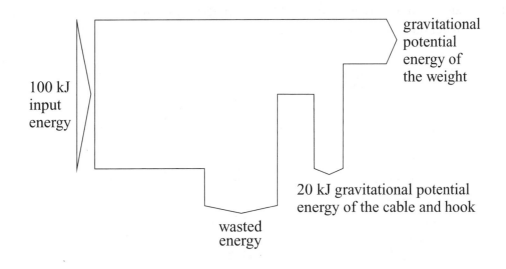

a) Suggest **one** type of energy that contributes to the energy wasted by the winch.

.......Sound...

[1]

b) The winch wastes a total of 50 kJ.
    Calculate the gravitational potential energy transferred to the weight by the winch.

                    Gravitational potential energy transferred to the weight = ...20........ kJ

[1]

c) The weight is released and falls to the ground. 1.5 kJ of energy is transferred into heat and sound
    energy during the fall due to the air resistance on the weight. Sketch and label a Sankey diagram
    to show the energy transfers that take place during the weight's fall.

[3]

[Total 5 marks]

Score: ☐

10

Heat Transfer

1   Three flasks, each containing 100 ml of water, are placed in closed boxes filled with a clear gel at an initial temperature of 50 °C. The water in each flask is at a different temperature, as shown.

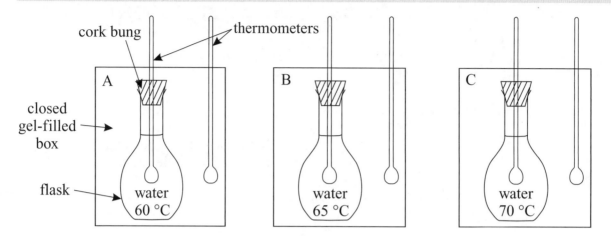

a) Name **two** ways in which the flasks will transfer heat to the gel surrounding them.

1. Radiation

2. Convection

                                                             [2]

b) State which flask will transfer heat to the gel the fastest. Explain your answer.

C, becaus they have more energy allowing the heat to transfer quicker

                                                             [2]

[Total 4 marks]

2   A solid block is heated at one end until the temperature of the whole block has increased.

a) Name the method of heat transfer in solids. Describe, in terms of particles, how energy is transferred through the solid block by this method.

Conduction, the particles with the most heat energy vibrate vigorously this transfers from particle to particle heating the block

                                                             [3]

b) The block also radiates thermal energy. Describe the process of radiation.

                                                             [1]

[Total 4 marks]

Score:

8

Heat Convection

1 Heat can be transferred by convection.

a) Place a cross next to the type of substance in which convection **cannot** take place.

solid	✗
liquid	
gas	

Give a reason for your answer.

The particles cannot freely move

[2]

b) A student is carrying out an experiment in class to demonstrate convection.
She fills a rectangular glass tube with water and heats one of the bottom corners, as shown.

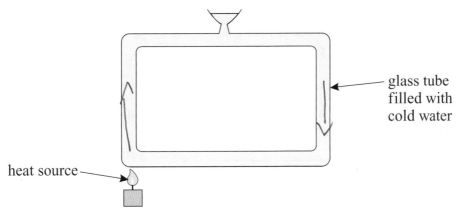

glass tube filled with cold water

heat source

i) Draw **two** arrows on the diagram above to show the movement of the water within the pipe.

[1]

ii) Explain why the water in the pipe moves in the way that you have shown in part i).

the hot particles rise and as they move away from the heat source the cool as cold particles fall this creates a circular motion

[3]

c) Which of the following is **not** an example of convection?
Place a cross in the appropriate box to indicate your answer.

☐ The heating of a large room by a radiator.　　☐ The heating of water in a kettle.

☑ The transfer of heat through a copper pan.　　☐ A hot air balloon rising.

[1]

[Total 7 marks]

Exam Practice Tip

An exam favourite is to show you a situation and get you to explain how convection is involved. Just remember that whatever kind of gas or liquid is involved, the process is pretty much always the same — the hot stuff rises, the cold stuff sinks and gets heated, and the whole thing repeats.

Score

☐

7

Reducing Energy Transfers

1 When humans are cold, the hairs on their bodies stand on end.

a) Explain how this reduces heat loss from the body.

....

....

[2]

b) Suggest and explain **one** other way in which heat loss can be reduced from the human body.

....

....

[2]

[Total 4 marks]

2 A homeowner is worried that her house is losing a lot of heat energy through its walls and windows.

a) The outer walls of the house are made up of two layers of bricks separated by an air cavity.

i) Which type of energy transfer does having an air gap in the wall help to reduce?
Place a cross in the appropriate box to indicate your answer.

Conduction	
Convection	
Radiation	

[1]

ii) The homeowner is considering having cavity wall insulation installed. State **one** type of energy transfer this will help to reduce. Explain your answer.

....

....

[1]

b) Suggest **two** ways in which heat loss through or around windows can be reduced.
Explain how each of your suggestions will help reduce heat loss.

1. ....

....

2. ....

....

[4]

[Total 6 marks]

Score:

10

Work and Power

1 Use words from the box to complete the passage below.

matter	energy	rate	newtons	watts	joules	act

Power is the ....a c t.......................... of doing work, or how much

.... is transferred per second. It is measured in

....

[Total 3 marks]

2 A student kicks a football, transferring 50 J of energy to the ball.

a) i) State what is meant by the **work done** by a force.

....

....
[1]

ii) How much work does the student do when she kicks the ball? State the correct unit.

Work done = ... unit ....
[1]

b) i) State the equation linking work done, force and distance moved in the direction of the force.

....
[1]

ii) The student kicks the ball along the ground with a force of 250 N.
Calculate the distance over which her foot is in contact with the ball.

Distance = ... m
[2]
[Total 5 marks]

3   A student builds a model boat with a 1 litre petrol tank and a 150 W petrol motor.

a) Calculate the energy that the model boat transfers in 10 minutes.

Remember, energy transferred is the same as work done.

Energy transferred = ... kJ

[2]

b) The motor provides a driving force of 155 N.
Calculate work done by the motor to move the boat 1.2 m.

Work done = ... J

[2]

c) The boat's motor is replaced with a motor that has a higher power, but the same fuel efficiency.
State and explain how you would expect this change to affect the maximum speed and how often
the boat will need refuelling.

....

....

....

....

....

[4]

[Total 8 marks]

4   Two students each drag identical tyres as far as they can in one go, along the same bit of ground.
The table shows the time taken and the distance each student dragged their tyre.

Student	Distance in m	Time taken in s
1	30	60
2	10	10

Student 1 concludes:

I dragged the tyre further and for longer, so I was more powerful than student 2.

Do you agree or disagree? Explain your answer.

....

....

....

....

[Total 3 marks]

Score:

19

Kinetic and Gravitational Potential Energy

1 Place a cross in the appropriate box to indicate the correct ending for each of the following sentences.

a) Kinetic energy is the energy an object has due to its

☐ movement.   ☐ temperature.   ☐ height.   ☐ charge.

[1]

b) When an object is lifted,

☐ work is done to convert gravitational potential energy into kinetic energy.

☐ work is done to convert kinetic energy into gravitational potential energy.

☐ work is done to convert gravitational potential energy into thermal energy.

☐ no work is done.

[1]

c) A bird in flight has

☐ gravitational potential energy only.

☐ kinetic energy only.

☐ gravitational potential energy and kinetic energy.

☐ neither kinetic energy nor gravitational potential energy.

[1]

[Total 3 marks]

2 A student throws a ball with a mass of 100 g directly upwards. The student catches the ball when it drops back down to the original height it was thrown from. At its highest point, the ball has a gravitational potential energy of 4.0 J.

a) How much kinetic energy will the ball have just before it reaches the student's hand, assuming no air resistance acts on the ball?

Kinetic energy = ... J
[1]

b) State the equation that links kinetic energy, mass and speed.

....

[1]

c) Calculate the speed of the ball just before it is caught.

Speed = ... m/s
[3]

[Total 5 marks]

Section 4 — Energy Resources and Energy Transfer

3 A roller coaster cart with a mass of 105 kg is rolling along a horizontal track at 2.39 m/s.

2.39 m/s

a) Calculate the kinetic energy of the cart.

Kinetic energy = ... J

[3]

b) The cart reaches a downhill slope in the track with a vertical height of 20.2 m.
It rolls down the slope with no driving force other than gravity.

i) State the equation that links gravitational potential energy, mass, acceleration of free fall (*g*)
and height.

....

[1]

ii) Calculate the gravitational potential energy lost by the cart as it rolls down the slope.

g = 10 m/s². You'll be given the value for g on an equations page in the exam, so you don't need to learn it.

Gravitational potential energy = ... J

[2]

iii)Assuming no friction acts against the cart, explain what happens to the gravitational potential
energy that is lost.

....

[1]

c) Calculate the speed of the cart at the bottom of the slope, assuming no friction acts
against the cart.

Remember the cart had some kinetic energy before the drop.

Speed = ... m/s

[4]

[Total 11 marks]

Score:

19

Non-Renewable Energy and Power Stations

1 Non-renewable energy sources can be used to generate electricity.

a) Which of the following energy sources is **not** a non-renewable energy source?
Place a cross in the appropriate box to indicate your answer.

☐ coal ☐ nuclear ☐ wind ☐ oil
[1]

b) Natural gas is a non-renewable energy source. Natural gas is burned in power stations to transfer the chemical energy of the gas into heat energy. Describe the process and the energy transfers that occur in a natural gas power station to transfer this heat energy into electrical energy.

....

....

....

....
[3]

PAPER 2

c) Describe **two** advantages of generating electricity using natural gas.

1. ....

....

2. ....

....
[2]

PAPER 2

d) A student says:

> Burning natural gas releases sulfur dioxide, which causes acid rain. This can harm plants and other wildlife.

i) Do you agree or disagree? Explain your answer.

....

....
[1]

ii) Other than damaging the environment, give **one** disadvantage of using natural gas to generate electricity.

....
[1]

[Total 8 marks]

Score: ☐

8

Nuclear, Wind and Geothermal Energy

1 In a nuclear power station, water is heated to produce steam.

a) Describe the energy transfer(s) that occur in a nuclear power station to produce the steam.

....

PAPER 2   *[1]*

b) i) One argument for building more nuclear power stations is that generating electricity from nuclear fuel does not contribute to global warming. Explain why this is the case.

....

....
                                                                                                                                    [2]

ii) Give **two** ways in which generating nuclear power can harm the environment.

1. ....

....

2. ....

....
                                                                                                                                    [2]
                                                                                                                        [Total 5 marks]

2 Electricity can be generated using wind and geothermal energy.

a) i) Complete the chart to show the energy transfers when generating electricity using a wind turbine.

.... → .... → ....

   energy of the turbine   energy of the generator   energy in wires

PAPER 2   *[3]*

ii) Give **one** advantage and **one** disadvantage of generating electricity using wind.

....

....

PAPER 2   *[2]*

b) Give **one** advantage and **one** disadvantage of generating electricity using geothermal resources.

....

....
                                                                                                                                    [2]
                                                                                                                        [Total 7 marks]

Score:

12

Solar and Wave Energy

1 In some coastal regions, electricity is generated from waves using wave converters.

a) Name the type of energy that is converted into electrical energy in wave converters.

....
[1]

PAPER 2

b) A student claims:

> Using waves is a reliable method of generating electricity that has low set-up costs and running costs.

Do you agree or disagree? Explain your answer.

....

....

....
[2]
[Total 3 marks]

2 Energy from the Sun is used in different ways.

a) Name **one** device used to transfer energy from the Sun directly into electrical energy.

....
[1]

b) Electricity generated from the Sun's energy can be used to heat water in a home. Describe **one** other way the Sun's energy can be used to heat water in a home.

....

....
[1]

PAPER 2

c) Give **two** reasons why electricity generated from the Sun is rarely supplied to the National Grid.

....

....

....
[2]
[Total 4 marks]

Score: ☐

7

Generating Electricity Using Water

1 Water can be used in many ways to generate electricity. In some countries, electricity is generated using hydroelectric dams. Water is held back behind the dam before being allowed to flow out through turbines to produce electricity.

a) Describe the energy transfers involved when water flowing through the turbines is used to produce electricity.

....

....

[2]

PAPER 2

b) Hydroelectric power stations don't produce any carbon dioxide when generating electricity. Give **two** ways that using hydroelectric power stations to generate electricity damages the environment.

1. ....

....

2. ....

....

[2]

c) In some hydroelectric power stations, electrical energy is used to pump water back into the reservoir during times of low electricity demand. Give the name of this type of system.

....

[1]

PAPER 2

d) Sea tides can also be used to generate electricity using tidal barrages. Give **two** advantages of generating electricity using tidal barrages.

1. ....

....

2. ....

....

[2]

[Total 7 marks]

Score:

7

Pressure and Density

1   A student has a collection of metal toy soldiers of different sizes made from the same metal.

a) Which of the following statements is true?
Place a cross in the appropriate box to indicate your answer.

☐ The masses and densities of each of the toy soldiers are the same.

☐ The masses of each of the toy soldiers are the same, but their densities may vary.

☐ The densities of each of the toy soldiers are the same, but their masses may vary.

☐ The densities and masses of each toy soldier may vary.

[1]

b) The student wants to measure the density of one of the toy soldiers.
He can use the equipment shown.

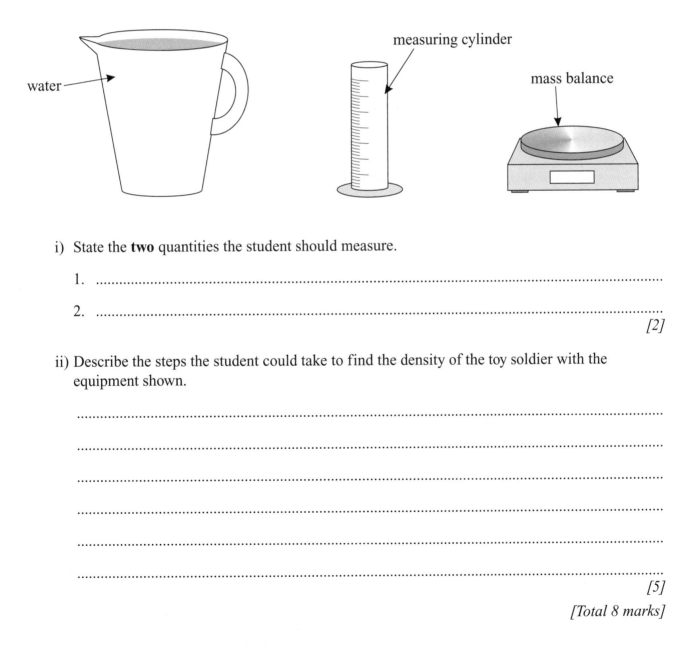

i) State the **two** quantities the student should measure.

1. ....

2. ....

[2]

ii) Describe the steps the student could take to find the density of the toy soldier with the equipment shown.

....

....

....

....

....

....

[5]

[Total 8 marks]

2 Pressure is a measure of the force applied to the surface of a substance.

a) Use words from the box to complete the passage.

equal	smaller	different	greater

In gases and liquids at rest, the pressure at any point is .... in all directions.

The pressure is .... the deeper the gas or liquid gets.

[2]

b) i) State the equation linking pressure, force and area.

....

[1]

ii) Calculate the pressure created by a force of 18 N acting over an area of 0.45 m²

Pressure = ... Pa

[2]

[Total 5 marks]

3 A company that manufactures a water-resistant digital watch tests the watch under high pressure. They only recommend it is used underwater if the pressure difference from the surface is 240 kPa or less.

a) State the equation linking pressure difference, height, density and the acceleration due to gravity (*g*).

....

[1]

b) i) The mass of a 0.5 m³ volume of water is 500 kg. Calculate the density of water.

Density = ... unit ....

[4]

ii) Calculate the maximum depth from the surface of the water that the watch can be used at.

Remember that the pressure is in kPa. You'll need to convert it to do this calculation.

Maximum depth = ... m

[3]

[Total 8 marks]

Exam Practice Tip

It's important to remember with questions like the last one that it's the height **difference** that matters. If you climb to an altitude of 4000 m and want to know the pressure difference from when you started, the first thing to ask is "what was my initial altitude?" Don't just plug 4000 into the equation if you didn't start at 0.

Score

[   ]

21

Changes of State

1 Substances can exist in different states of matter.

a) i) Describe the arrangement and movement of the particles in a solid.

....

....
[2]

ii) Give the name of the state of matter that possesses the **highest** average energy per particle.

....
[1]

b) If a substance is heated to a certain temperature it can change from a solid to a liquid.

i) Give the name of this process.

....
[1]

ii) Explain why the temperature rising above a certain level causes this process to happen.

....

....

....
[2]

c) If a liquid is heated to a certain temperature it starts to boil and become a gas.

i) Name the other process that causes a liquid to start to become a gas. Explain how it is different to boiling.

....

....

....

....
[3]

ii) Explain why the remaining liquid cools down when a liquid starts to turn into a gas by the process named in part i).

When a liquid evaporates, the fastest particles are more likely to...

....

....
[3]
[Total 12 marks]

Score: ⬚

12

😐 ⬚   🙂 ⬚   😊 ⬚

Particle Theory and Temperature in Gases

1   The Kelvin scale and the Celsius scale are two scales that can be used to measure temperature.

a) i) A gas is cooled. Describe what effect this has on the average speed of its particles.

....

[1]

ii) Explain why there is a minimum possible temperature that any substance can reach, known as the absolute zero of temperature.

....

....

[2]

iii) Give the numerical value of the absolute zero of temperature in degrees Celsius.

Temperature = ... °C

[1]

b) Temperature can be converted between the Kelvin and Celsius scales. Complete the table below.

Temperature (K)	Temperature (°C)
10	....
....	631

[2]

[Total 6 marks]

2   A study of smoke particles in air shows that they appear to move with a random motion.

a) i) Give the name of this type of motion.

....

[1]

ii) Explain how this motion supports the particle theory of gases.

....

....

....

[2]

PAPER 2

b)   The temperature in kelvins of the air increases by a factor of three. Describe how the average kinetic energy of the air particles will change, and by what factor.

....

[1]

[Total 4 marks]

Score:

10

Particle Theory and Pressure in Gases

1   A sealed balloon contains 0.014 m³ of gas at a pressure of 98 kPa.

   a) i) The balloon is squeezed and its volume decreases. State the effect on the air pressure inside
          the balloon. Explain your answer in terms of particle theory.

....

....

....
                                                                                                              [3]

   ii) The balloon is compressed to 0.013 m³. The temperature of the air inside it remains constant.
       Calculate the air pressure inside the balloon after the compression.

Pressure = ... kPa
                                                                                                              [3]

   b) The air inside the balloon is gradually heated and it starts to expand. Explain why this happens.

....

....

....
                                                                                                              [3]

                                                                                              [Total 9 marks]

PAPER 2

2   A sealed container with a fixed volume is fitted with internal temperature and pressure gauges.
     The gauges show that the temperature is 288 K and the pressure is 107 kPa inside the container.

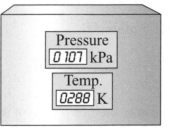

   The container is heated so that the temperature of the gas inside it becomes 405 K.
   Calculate the pressure that will be shown on the pressure gauge.

Pressure = ... kPa
                                                                                              [Total 3 marks]

                                                                                              Score:

                                                                                                12

Section 6 — Magnetism and Electromagnetism

Magnets and Magnetic Fields

1   A student draws the magnetic field lines between four bar magnets, as shown in the diagram.

   a)   Describe an experiment that the student could have done to show this magnetic field pattern.

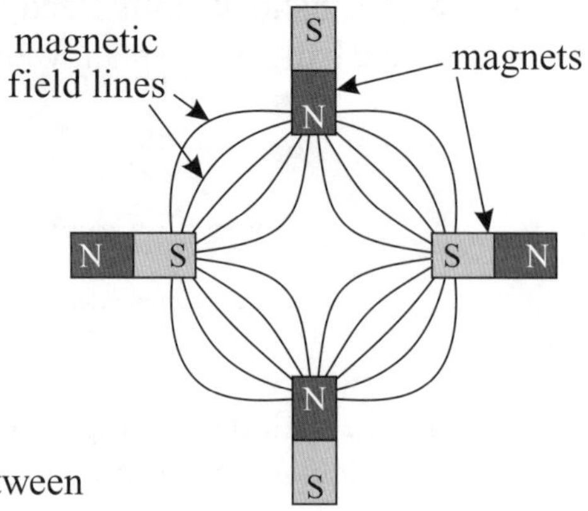

     ....

     ....

     ....

     ....

                                           [2]

   b)   Add **four** arrows to magnetic field lines on the diagram, one between each set of magnets, to show the direction of the magnetic field.

                                           [2]

   c)   The student arranges two of the magnets as shown below.

     N   S   N   S

     i)   Describe the magnetic field in the shaded region between the dotted lines.

     ....

PAPER 2   *[1]*

     ii)   State whether there will be a force of attraction, repulsion, or no force between the two magnets. Explain your answer.

     ....

     ....

                                           [2]

                               [Total 7 marks]

PAPER 2

2   Iron and steel are both magnetic materials.

   a)   Describe what is meant by a **magnetic material**.

     ....

                                           [1]

   b)   The head of an iron nail is placed close to the north pole of a bar magnet. The head of the nail is attracted towards the bar magnet until they touch and it sticks to the magnet. Explain what causes this to happen.

     ....

     ....

     ....

                                           [2]

                               [Total 3 marks]

Score:

10

Electromagnetism

1 A student investigating magnetic fields passes a copper rod through a piece of flat card and connects it in an electrical circuit, as shown in the diagram.

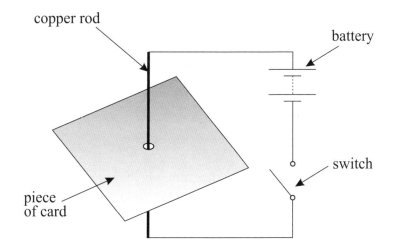

a) Place a cross in the appropriate box to indicate your answer.
When the switch is closed

☐ a magnetic field is created around the copper rod.

☐ a magnetic field is created by the piece of card.

☐ the piece of card becomes magnetic.

☐ no magnetic field is created.

[1]

PAPER 2

b) Some iron filings are sprinkled onto the card. When the switch is closed, a pattern develops in the iron filings. On the diagram above, sketch the magnetic field that causes this pattern.

[1]

PAPER 2

c) The student removes the rod and card and attaches a loop of wire passed through a piece of card to the electrical circuit with the switch closed. Sketch the magnetic field around the wire on the piece of card, showing the pattern of the magnetic field.

[1]

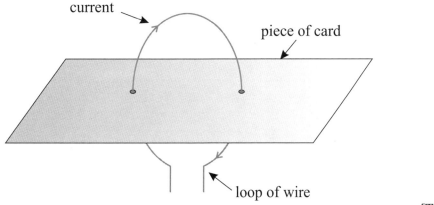

[Total 3 marks]

Section 6 — Magnetism and Electromagnetism

PAPER 2

2   An electromagnet is used by a crane to lift, move and drop iron and steel.

a) Describe the basic structure of an electromagnet.

....

[1]

b) Describe the shape of the magnetic field that an electromagnet produces.
    You may use a sketch to help with your answer.

....

....

....

[2]

c) When a current is passed through the electromagnet, an iron bar on the ground nearby is attracted
    to it. When the current is stopped, the bar drops back to the ground. Explain why this happens.

....

....

....

....

[4]

d) The crane's electromagnet contains a magnetically soft iron core.

    i) Describe what is meant by a **magnetically soft** material.

    ....

    ....

    [1]

    ii) Explain why putting a magnetically hard core in the electromagnet would cause the
        electromagnet to not work properly.

    ....

    ....

    [2]

    [Total 10 marks]

    Score:

    13

The Motor Effect

1   The diagram shows an experiment in which a current is passed through a wire in a magnetic field.

a)   A force acts on the loop of wire causing it to move.

   i)   Explain why this happens.

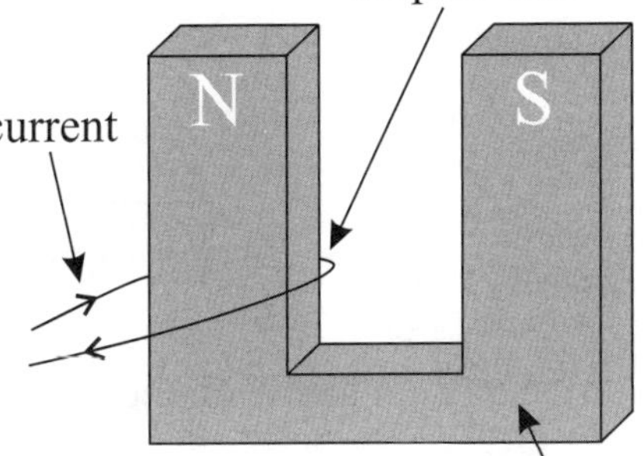

....

....

....

....

....
[1]

loop of wire

current

N   S

magnet

Use Fleming's left-hand rule.

   ii)   State the direction in which the loop will move.

....
[1]

b)   i)   State what effect increasing the current will have on the force on the loop of wire.

....
[1]

   ii)   Give **two** ways in which the direction that the force acts could be reversed in this experiment.

   1.   ....

....

   2.   ....

....
[2]

PAPER 2

c)   The diagram below shows a free-rolling conducting bar on a set of fixed conducting bars
in a magnetic field. All of the conducting bars have a current flowing through them.
Explain, in terms of electron movement, why the free-rolling conducting bar doesn't move.

....

....

....

....

....
[2]

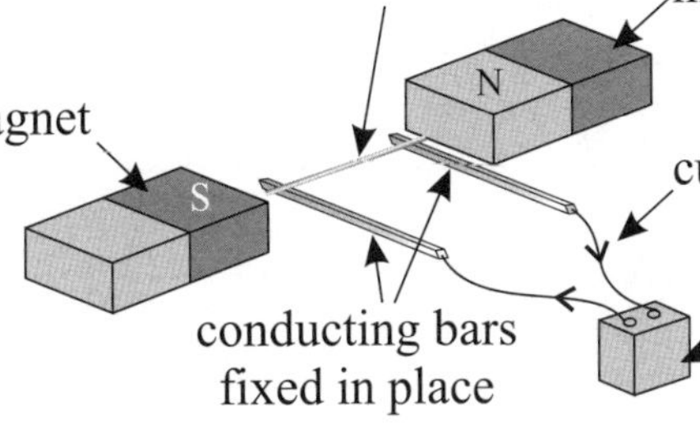

conducting bar
that is free to roll

magnet

N

magnet

current

power
source

conducting bars
fixed in place

[Total 7 marks]

Score:

7

Electric Motors and Loudspeakers

1   A student is building a simple d.c. motor. He starts by putting a loop of current-carrying wire that is free to rotate about an axis in a magnetic field, as shown in the diagram.

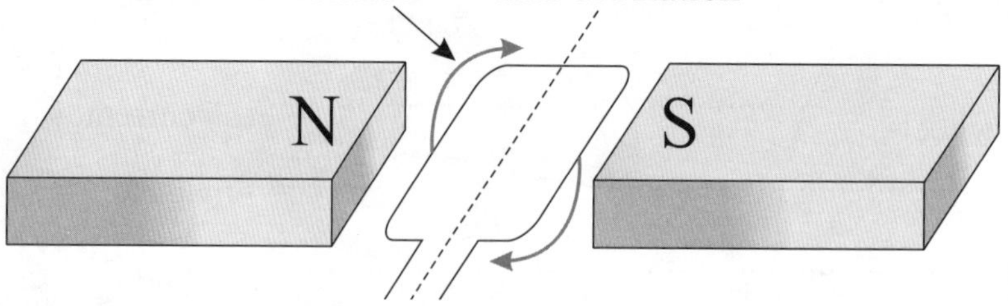

direction of rotation   axis of rotation

N   S

a) Draw an arrow on the diagram to show the direction of the current in the wire.
Use Fleming's left-hand rule.
[1]

b) The starting position of the loop is shown in the diagram. Explain why the motor will stop rotating in the same direction after 90° of rotation from its start position.

....

....
[1]

c) Suggest and explain how the student could get the motor to keep rotating in the same direction.

....

....
[2]

d) Give **one** way the motor could be made to rotate faster.

....
[1]
[Total 5 marks]

2   The diagram shows the parts inside an earphone. Sound waves are caused by mechanical vibrations. Explain how the earphone uses an a.c. supply to produce sound waves.

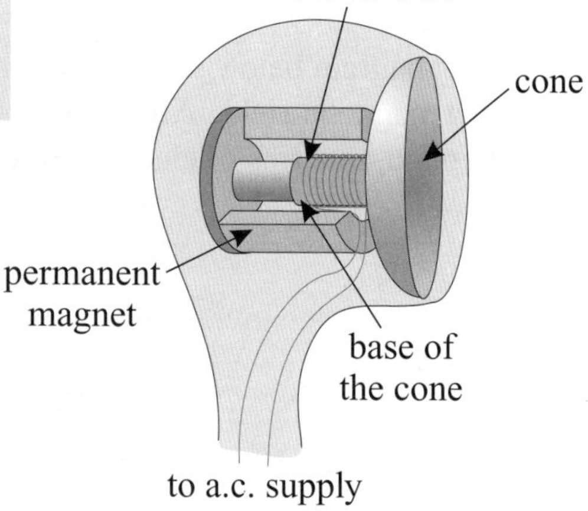

coil of wire

cone

permanent magnet

base of the cone

to a.c. supply

....

....

....

....

....

....

....

[Total 4 marks]

Score: ☐

9

Electromagnetic Induction

1   A student uses the rotation of a hamster wheel to power a battery charger.

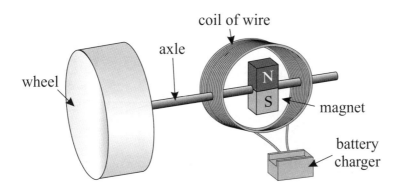

a) Explain how rotating the wheel creates a voltage across the battery charger.

....

....

....

[2]

b) Give **two** ways the voltage created across the battery charger could be increased.

1.   ....

....

2.   ....

....

[2]

c) The student makes the following claim.

My hamster will charge the battery if it runs in either direction round the wheel.

Do you agree or disagree? Explain your answer.

....

....

[1]

[Total 5 marks]

2   The diagram shows a wind-up a.c. generator that uses electromagnetic induction to generate an alternating current. The generator is connected to an oscilloscope. The slip rings make sure that each end of the coil remains connected to the same oscilloscope wire.

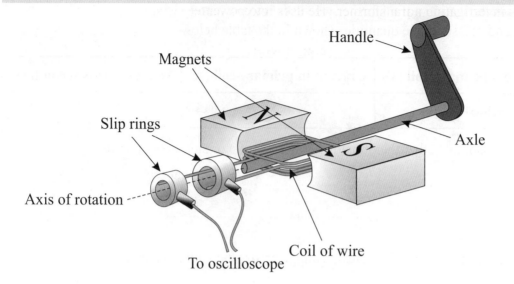

When the handle is rotated clockwise at a constant speed, the oscilloscope shows the trace below.

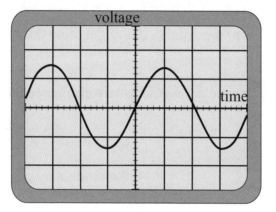

a) Describe how rotating the handle of the generator causes an a.c. voltage to be produced in the circuit connected to the oscilloscope.

    ....

    ....

    [2]

b) Sketch on the diagram a trace that you could see if the handle was rotated faster.

    [2]

c) Describe the trace that you would expect to see if the position of the coil was fixed and the magnets were rotated around the axis of rotation shown in the diagram at the original speed.

    ....

    [1]

    [Total 5 marks]

Exam Practice Tip

Electromagnetic induction is basically the opposite of the motor effect — movement causes a voltage and (sometimes) a current. A.c. generators are used to produce loads of the electricity we use, so you might see them applied to all sorts of contexts. Just look out for a changing magnetic field or a moving magnet or wire.

Score

10

Transformers

1   A student is investigating a transformer. He uses it to power
a spotlight, and measures the quantities shown in the table below.

Voltage across primary coil (V)	Current in primary coil (A)	Voltage across secondary coil (V)
240	0.25	12

a)   State, with a reason, whether the transformer is a step-up or step-down transformer.

....

....

                                 [1]

b)   i)   State the equation linking power, current and voltage.

....

                                 [1]

    ii) Calculate the input power to the primary coil when using the spotlight.

Power = ... W

                                 [2]

    iii) Calculate the current in the secondary coil when using the spotlight.
       Assume the transformer is 100% efficient.

Current = ... A

                                 [3]

c)   The student makes the following claim.

> The core of a transformer has to be made of a conducting
> material such as iron so the current can travel through it.

Do you agree or disagree? Explain your answer.

....

....

                                 [1]

                      [Total 8 marks]

2 The National Grid is a network that transmits electricity around the country. The diagram shows a step-up transformer used in the National Grid. The secondary coil has 16 times more turns on it than the primary coil.

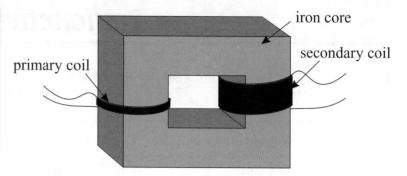

a) Explain how transformers are used in the National Grid to transmit electricity from power stations efficiently and supply the electricity to the consumer safely.

....

....

....

....

....

[3]

b) i) State the equation linking the number of turns on the primary and secondary coils of a transformer and the voltages across the primary and secondary coils.

....

[1]

ii) The voltage across the primary coil is 25 000 V.
Calculate the voltage across the secondary coil.

Voltage = ... V

[4]

c) Explain why a transformer wouldn't work if a direct current was supplied to the primary coil.

....

....

....

[3]

[Total 11 marks]

Score:

19

Radioactivity

1 Iodine-131 ($^{131}_{53}$I) is an unstable isotope of iodine.

a) i) Complete the table for an atom of iodine-131.

Particle	Charge	Number present in an atom of iodine-131
Proton	positive	
Neutron	zero	
Electron		53

[3]

ii) Name the particle(s) found in the nucleus of an atom.

....

[1]

b) What is meant by the term **isotopes**? Place a cross in the appropriate box to indicate your answer.

☐ Atoms with the same atomic number but a different mass number.

☐ Atoms with the same mass number but a different atomic number.

☐ Atoms with the same proton number but a different atomic number.

☐ Atoms with the same number of neutrons but a different number of electrons.

[1]

c) Iodine-131 is a waste product of some nuclear power plants and it contributes to the low level of radiation that is present all around us all the time.

i) Give the name of this low level of radiation.

....

[1]

ii) Give **two** natural sources of this low level of radiation.

1. ....

2. ....

[2]

d) Name **three** types of radiation that can be given out when unstable nuclei decay.

....

[3]

[Total 11 marks]

Score: ☐

11

The Three Kinds of Radioactivity

1   Alpha, beta and gamma radiation are all types of nuclear radiation.
     All three types of nuclear radiation can cause ionisation.

   a) i) State the name of an atom that has been ionised.

   ....
                                                                                                                              [1]

   ii) State which type of nuclear radiation is the most strongly ionising. Explain your answer.

   ....

   ....
                                                                                                                              [2]

   b) i) Name the type of nuclear radiation that is a type of electromagnetic radiation.

   ....
                                                                                                                              [1]

   ii) Name the type of nuclear radiation whose particles are electrons.

   ....
                                                                                                                              [1]

                                                                                                                [Total 5 marks]

2   Alpha, beta and gamma radiation sources were used to pass radiation through thin sheets of paper
     and aluminium. A detector was used to measure where radiation had passed through the sheets.
     The results are shown below.

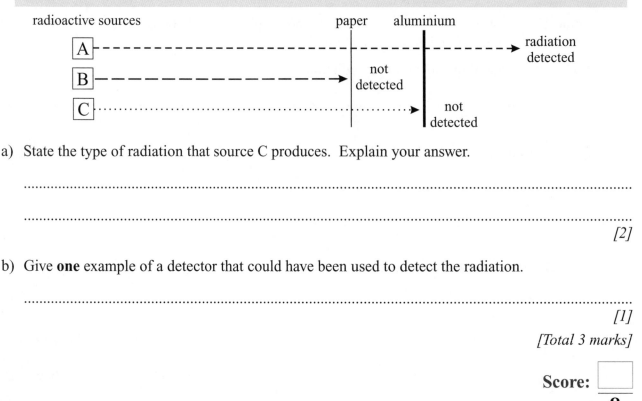

   a) State the type of radiation that source C produces. Explain your answer.

   ....

   ....
                                                                                                                              [2]

   b) Give **one** example of a detector that could have been used to detect the radiation.

   ....
                                                                                                                              [1]

                                                                                                                [Total 3 marks]

                                                                                                      Score:

                                                                                                                    8

Alpha Scattering and Nuclear Equations

1 Alpha particles are fired towards a gold nucleus ($^{197}_{79}$Au) and a silver nucleus ($^{107}_{47}$Ag) as shown in the diagram below. The amount of deflection of the alpha particles is measured.

a) State which nucleus will deflect the alpha particles more. Explain your answer.

....

....

[1]

b) The speed of the alpha particles directed at the gold nucleus is increased.
Describe what effect this will have on how much the particles are deflected by the gold nucleus.

....

[1]

c) The beam of alpha particles is moved so that it doesn't pass as close to the gold nucleus.
Describe what effect this will have on how much the particles are deflected by the gold nucleus.

....

[1]

[Total 3 marks]

2 In the early 1900s, the results of Geiger and Marsden's gold-foil experiment led Ernest Rutherford to come up with the nuclear model of the atom.

a) Describe Rutherford's nuclear model of the atom.

....

....

....

....

[3]

b) Describe Geiger and Marsden's gold-foil experiment.

....

....

....

[2]

c) Explain how the results of the Geiger and Marsden experiment support the nuclear model of the atom.

With longer answer questions, take your time and read your answer at the end to make sure it makes sense and answers the question.

....

....

....

....

....

....

[3]

[Total 8 marks]

3   Nuclear equations show what is produced when unstable nuclei decay.

A beta particle can also be written as β.

a) i) Complete the symbol of a beta particle.

$$\overset{\cdots\cdots}{\underset{\cdots\cdots}{}} e$$

[2]

ii) Describe what happens to the atomic number and the mass number of a nucleus when it undergoes beta decay.

....

....

[2]

b) i) Describe what happens to the atomic number and the mass number of a nucleus when it undergoes gamma decay.

....

....

[2]

ii) Complete this nuclear equation, which shows a polonium isotope decaying by alpha and gamma emission.

An alpha particle can be written as He or α.

$$\overset{\cdots\cdots}{\underset{\cdots\cdots}{}} Po \longrightarrow \overset{195}{\underset{82}{}} Pb + \overset{\cdots\cdots}{\underset{\cdots\cdots}{}} \alpha + \overset{\cdots\cdots}{} \gamma$$

[4]

[Total 10 marks]

Score:

21

Half-Life

1   A student measured how the activity of a radioactive sample changed with time and used her data to calculate its half-life. Before getting the sample out of storage she measured the activity in the laboratory. When processing the data she subtracted this value from all her activity readings.

a) Suggest why the student recorded the activity in the laboratory before starting the experiment.

....

....

                                    [2]

b) The table below shows the student's processed data.
Use the grid to plot a graph of the data. Draw a curved line of best fit.

Use a sharp pencil to draw a neat graph.

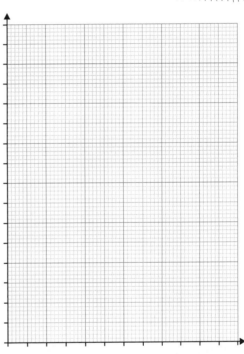

Time (mins)	Adjusted activity (Bq)
0	740
10	610
20	490
30	400
40	330
60	210
80	140

[5]

c) Use your graph to find the half-life of the sample.

Half-life = ... minutes

[2]

d) All of the radioactive samples that the laboratory uses are all identical when new. The student decides to repeat the experiment with a sample that is much older than the first. Explain what effect this might have on the data collected.

....

....

....

[2]

[Total 11 marks]

Section 7 — Radioactivity and Particles

88

2 Use words from the box to complete the passage below.

| electrons | decreases | all |
| nuclei | half | increases |

The radioactivity of a sample always .... over time.

The half-life is the time taken for .... of the unstable

.... now present to decay.

[Total 3 marks]

3 A radioactive isotope sample has a half-life of 40 seconds.

a) i) The initial activity of the sample is 8000 Bq. Calculate the activity after 2 minutes.

Activity = ... Bq
[2]

ii) Calculate the number of whole minutes it would take for the activity to fall below 200 Bq.

Time = ... mins
[3]

b) Chang and Paul are discussing half-lives.

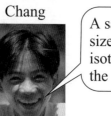

Chang: A sample of the same size but of a different isotope would have the same half-life.

Paul: A sample of the same size but of a different isotope would have a different half-life.

Which student is correct? Explain your answer.

....

....
[1]
[Total 6 marks]

Exam Practice Tip

There's quite a lot of maths involved in half-life questions. Try not to panic though. Just take your time and go through the different stages slowly. Make sure you show your workings for calculations or if you've used a graph. You then might still be able to pick up marks even if you get the final answer wrong. Bonus.

Score

20

Uses of Nuclear Radiation

1 An engineering company knows that one of its pipes is leaking somewhere between two points underground at their site. They are going to use a radioactive source with a short half-life as a tracer to identify the area where the pipe is leaking.

a) i) What type of radiation should the radioactive source they use emit? Place a cross in the correct box.

Alpha	
Beta	
Gamma	

[1]

ii) Explain your answer to part i).

....

....

[2]

b) Describe how the company could use the radioactive source to identify the area where the leak is occurring.

....

....

....

[3]

c) A student lives close to the site and has concerns about the company's use of radioactive tracers.

Using radioactive tracers near my home is dangerous — using them will expose me to a high level of radiation for many years.

Do you agree or disagree? Explain your answer.

....

....

....

[2]

[Total 8 marks]

2 Iodine-123 is commonly used as a tracer in medicine.

a) Describe how iodine-123 can be used to detect whether the thyroid gland is absorbing iodine as it normally should do.

....

....

....

[2]

b) Explain why alpha emitters cannot be used as tracers in medicine.

....

....

....

....

[4]

c) The table shows the properties of three other radioisotopes.

Radioisotope	Half-life	Type of emission
technetium-99m	6 hours	gamma
phosphorus-32	14 days	beta
cobalt-60	5 years	beta/gamma

State which of these would be best to use as a medical tracer. Explain your answer.

....

....

[2]

[Total 8 marks]

3 An ancient wooden artefact was found to have 1 part carbon-14 to 80 000 000 parts carbon. The half-life of carbon-14 is 5730 years and the ratio of carbon-14:carbon in living things is 1:10 000 000. Calculate the amount of time that has passed since the wood was living material.

After 1 half-life the artefact will have 1 part carbon-14 to 20 000 000 parts carbon.

Time = ... years

[Total 3 marks]

Score:

19

Risks from Nuclear Radiation

1   Some people are exposed to higher than average levels of ionising radiation while at work.

a) Explain why exposure to ionising radiation can be dangerous.

....

....

....
[2]

b) Radiotherapists in hospitals use some types of radiation as part of radiotherapy treatment.

i) Describe what is meant by **radiotherapy**.

....
[1]

ii) Describe **one** precaution that should be taken by radiotherapists to minimise their radiation exposure.

....
[1]

iii) Some radiotherapists have to handle radioactive sources in a laboratory.
Describe **two** safety precautions that should be taken when handling radioactive sources.

1. ....

....

2. ....

....
[2]

c) Nuclear power station employees work with nuclear fuel or radioactive waste.

i) Describe **one** precaution that should be taken by nuclear workers to reduce their radiation exposure.

....

....
[1]

ii) Suggest **one** reason why it is difficult to dispose of radioactive waste.

....

....
[1]

[Total 8 marks]

Score: ☐

8

Nuclear Fission

1   Nuclear fission takes place in nuclear reactors. The diagram shows the basic structure of a gas-cooled nuclear reactor.

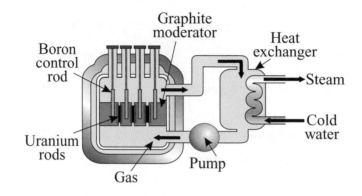

a) Give **one** fuel that can be used in a nuclear reactor.

....

[1]

b) i) Describe what happens during a single nuclear fission event and the products formed.

....

....

....

....

[4]

ii) Explain how nuclear fission can be used to produce energy continuously in a nuclear reactor, and how part of the nuclear reactor is designed to help this happen.

In a nuclear reactor, the neutrons released from each fission event collide with...

....

....

....

[3]

c) Explain the purpose of the control rods in a nuclear reactor.

....

....

[1]

[Total 9 marks]

Score:

9

Candidate Surname		Candidate Forename(s)

Centre Number	Candidate Number

Certificate
International GCSE

Physics
Paper 1P

Practice Paper
Time allowed: 2 hours

You must have:
- A ruler.
- A calculator.

Total marks:

Instructions to candidates
- Use **black** ink to write your answers.
- Write your name and other details in the spaces provided above.
- Answer **all** questions in the spaces provided.
- In calculations, show clearly how you worked out your answers.
- You will need to answer some questions by placing a cross in a box, like this: ☒
  To change your answer, draw a line through the box like this: ☒
  Then mark your new answer as normal.

Information for candidates
- The marks available are given in brackets at the end of each question.
- There are 120 marks available for this paper.
- You might find the equations on page 148 useful.

Advice for candidates
- Read all the questions carefully.
- Write your answers as clearly and neatly as possible.
- Keep in mind how much time you have left.

Get the answers

Your free Online Edition of this book includes the complete answers for this Exam Paper — you can even print them out. There's more info about how to get your Online Edition at the front of this book.

Answer **all** questions

1   At the start of a roller coaster ride a carriage is raised by a chain lift through a vertical height of 40 m to point A, as shown in the diagram. It is stopped at point A and then released to follow the track through points B, C and D.

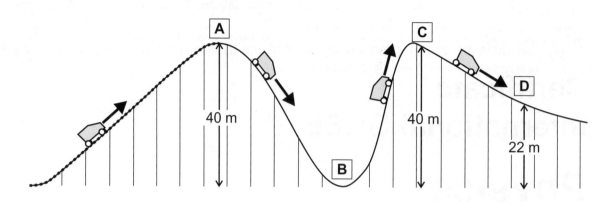

(a) (i) At which two points does the carriage have the same gravitational potential energy?
Place a cross (x) in the appropriate box to indicate your answer.

☐ B and D

☐ A and C

☐ C and D

☐ A and D

[1]

(ii) At which point does the car have the greatest kinetic energy?
Place a cross (x) in the appropriate box to indicate your answer.

☐ A

☐ B

☐ C

☐ D

[1]

(iii) What will happen to the car between points B and C?
Place a cross (x) in the appropriate box to indicate your answer.

☐ It will travel at a steady speed.

☐ It will reach its terminal velocity.

☐ It will decelerate.

☐ It will accelerate.

[1]

(b) The mass of the carriage and the people in it is 1500 kg.
The Earth's gravitational field strength is 10 N/kg.

(i) State the equation linking gravitational potential energy, mass, height and gravitational field strength.

....
[1]

(ii) Calculate the gain in gravitational potential energy (in kJ) of the carriage and people as they are raised by the chain lift to point A.

Gain in gravitational potential energy = ... kJ
[2]

(c) A different type of roller coaster uses a spring system to launch the carriage forward.
The springs used are elastic objects. State what is meant by an **elastic object**.

....

....
[1]

[Total 7 marks]

Turn over ▶

2   The diagram below shows a generator that is used to produce electricity in a coal-fired power station. The generator contains a coil of wire in a magnetic field.

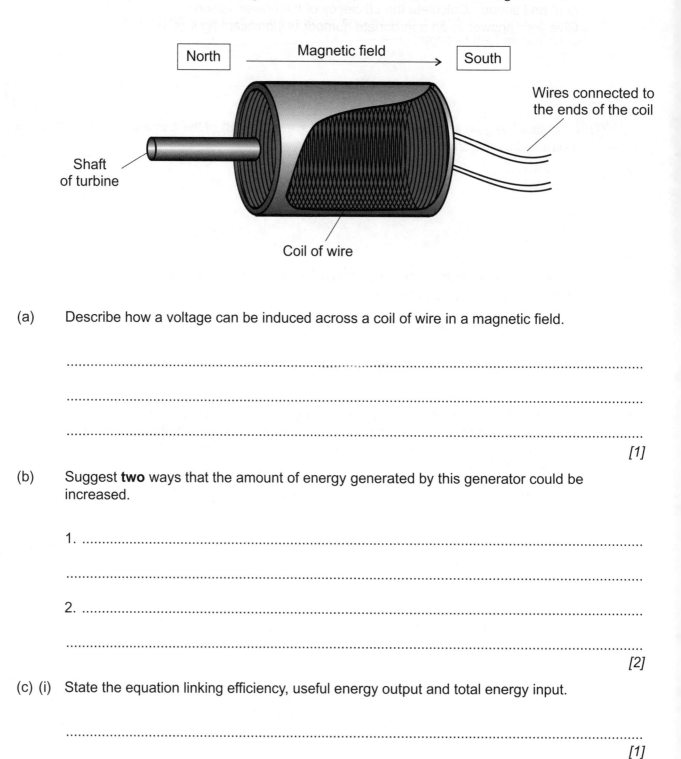

(a)   Describe how a voltage can be induced across a coil of wire in a magnetic field.

....

....

....

[1]

(b)   Suggest **two** ways that the amount of energy generated by this generator could be increased.

1. ....

....

2. ....

....

[2]

(c) (i)   State the equation linking efficiency, useful energy output and total energy input.

....

[1]

(ii) The generators in the power station produce a combined 180 MJ of electrical energy per second. However, the power station also wastes 415 MJ of energy every second, mainly as heat and sound. Calculate the efficiency of the power station.
Give your answer to an appropriate number of significant figures.

Efficiency = ...

[3]

(d) Coal-fired power stations are one of the many types of power station that supply the UK alternating current (a.c.) mains supply.

State what is meant by **alternating current (a.c.)**.

....

....

[1]

(e) Burning fossil fuels such as coal is a reliable method of generating a lot of electricity relatively cheaply.

Describe the disadvantages of burning coal to generate electricity.

....

....

....

....

[4]

[Total 12 marks]

Turn over ▶

Practice Paper 1P

3   Hot water tanks, like the one shown below, are used to heat and store water.

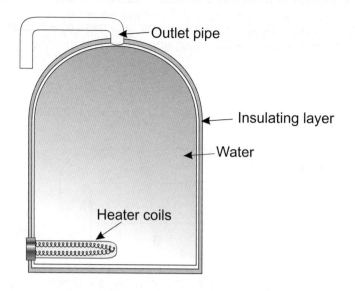

The heater coils have a current of 12 A flowing through them and a voltage of 230 V across them.

(a)   Calculate the amount of energy transferred from the coils to the water in 30 s.

Energy transferred = ... J

[2]

(b)   Describe how heat is transferred from the coils throughout the water in the tank.

....

....

....

....

....

[4]

A student wanted to model how the thickness of the insulating layer on a water tank affects how quickly the water in a tank cools.

She carried out an investigation to test how the thickness of a cotton wool jacket affects its ability to insulate. She used the following apparatus and method:

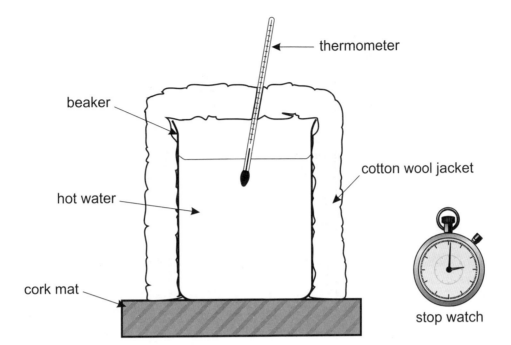

- Put 200 cm³ of boiling water in the glass beaker.

- Fit a 1 cm thick cotton wool jacket over the beaker.

- Put a thermometer into the beaker through the cotton wool jacket.

- Start the stop watch when the temperature cools to 95 °C.

- Record the temperature after three minutes.

- Repeat the experiment using jackets of 2, 3, 4 and 5 cm thickness.

(c) (i) Give **two** ways the student could make her results more precise.

1. ....

2. ....

[2]

(ii) Describe how the student could process her repeated results to get one value for the final water temperature after 3 minutes for each insulating layer.

....

....

[1]

Turn over ▶

Practice Paper 1P

(iii) The student's results are shown in the sketch below.

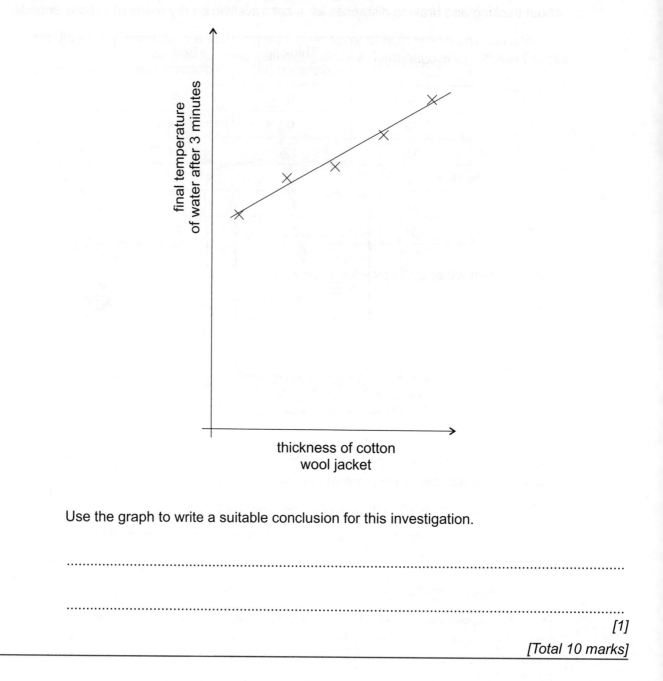

Use the graph to write a suitable conclusion for this investigation.

....

....

[1]

[Total 10 marks]

4 A driving instructor has been looking at the Highway Code. He has found the following data about thinking and braking distances for a car travelling on dry roads at various speeds.

Speed (m/s)	Thinking distance (m)	Braking distance (m)
9	6	6
13	9	14
18	12	24
22	15	38
27	18	55
31	21	75

(a) Calculate the stopping distance for a speed of 13 m/s.

Stopping distance = ... m

[1]

(b) The data in the table was obtained by observing a large number of drivers.
Explain why it was sensible to collect the data this way.

....

....

....

[2]

(c) Describe the different factors, other than speed, that can increase the stopping distance of a car. State whether each one affects the thinking distance or the braking distance.

....

....

....

....

....

....

[5]

[Total 8 marks]

Turn over ▶

5   An artificial satellite orbits the Earth in an almost circular path, as shown in the diagram. It takes 1 day to orbit the Earth.

(a)   Which of the following also orbits the Earth?
Place a cross (x) in the appropriate box to indicate your answer.

☐ a planet

☐ a star

☐ a moon

☐ a comet

[1]

(b)   Name the force that keeps the satellite in orbit around the Earth.

....

[1]

(c)   The satellite has an orbital speed of 3080 m/s. Calculate the radius of the satellite's orbit.

Radius = ... m

[3]

(d) The satellite sends microwave signals and visible light waves to Earth.

Describe the similarities and differences between visible light and microwaves.

....

....

....

....

....

[4]

[Total 9 marks]

Turn over ▶

6   A student measures the activity of a radioactive sample. He uses a detector to measure the activity of the sample every minute. His results are shown in the table.

Time (minutes)	0	1	2	3	4	5	6
Activity (becquerels)	80	60	45	34	25	19	14

(a)   Give **two** dangers of exposure to ionising radiation.

1. ....

2. ....

[2]

(b)   Suggest **one** piece of equipment that could have been used to measure the activity of the sample.

....

[1]

(c) (i)   Use this data to draw a graph on the grid below.
Draw a curved line of best fit.

[5]

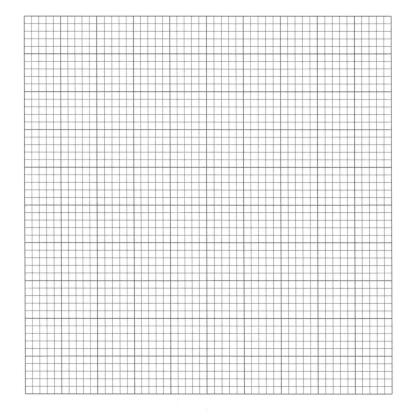

(ii)   Use the graph to find the half-life of this radioactive sample.

Half-life = ... min

[2]

(d)   After the experiment is finished the radioactive source is put into storage in another part of the building. The detector still picks up background radiation in the laboratory.

Give **four** sources that may contribute to this background radiation.

1. ....

....

2. ....

....

3. ....

....

4. ....

....

[4]

(e) (i)   Another radioactive isotope, radium-226, decays by alpha emission.
Fill in the blanks in the reaction below to show the alpha emission.

$$^{226}_{88}\text{Ra} \rightarrow \,^{222}_{.....}\text{Rn} + \,^{....}_{2}\alpha$$

[1]

(ii)   How many protons does the radium-226 (Ra) nucleus shown in part (i) have?
Place a cross (x) in the appropriate box to indicate your answer.

☐ 226

☐ 138

☐ 88

☐ 222

[1]

[Total 16 marks]

Turn over ▶

7   A student wanted to know how the current flowing through a filament lamp changes with the voltage across it. He set up this circuit.

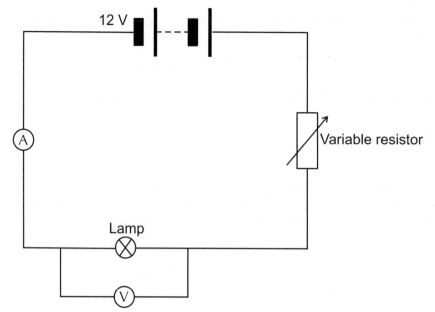

He used a variable resistor to change the voltage across the lamp.

Here is the graph he plotted of his results.

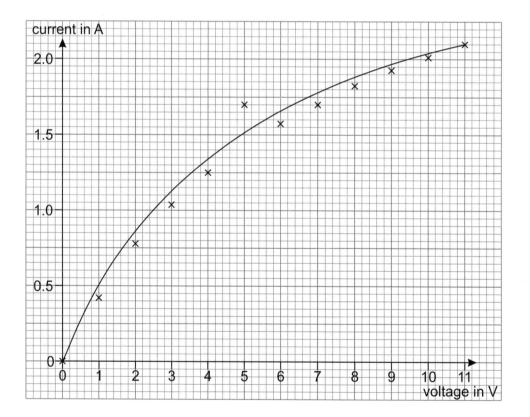

(a)   Give the dependent variable in this experiment.

....

[1]

(b) (i) Describe what the student has done wrong when drawing a line of best fit.

....

....

[1]

(ii) State the equation linking voltage, current and resistance.

....

[1]

(iii) The student corrects his line of best fit and uses it to work out that when the voltage across the lamp is 5 V, the current through it is 1.4 A.
Calculate the resistance of the lamp when the voltage across it is 5 V.

Resistance = ... unit ....

[3]

(c) The student makes the following claim.

The resistance of a filament bulb is constant.

Do you agree or disagree? Use the graph to explain your answer.

....

....

....

[2]

[Total 8 marks]

Turn over ▶

Practice Paper 1P

8   An engineering student has made a simple electric motor as shown in the diagram.

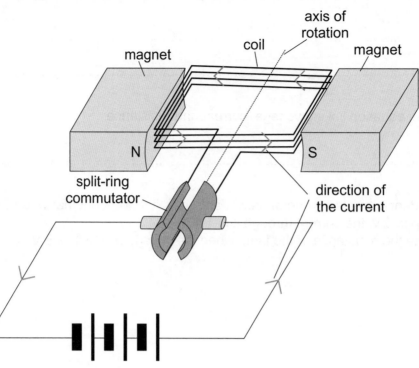

The split-ring commutator changes the direction of the current every half turn so that the motor will continue to rotate in the same direction.

(a)   The direction of the current is shown. State which direction the coil will rotate in.

....
[1]

(b)   Explain how the coil of wire in a simple electric motor turns.

....

....

....
[2]

(c)   The engineering student decides to make some changes to his motor.

Suggest **two** ways that he could speed up the rotation of the motor.

1. ....

....

2. ....

....
[2]

[Total 5 marks]

9   A hydraulic system is shown in the diagram below.

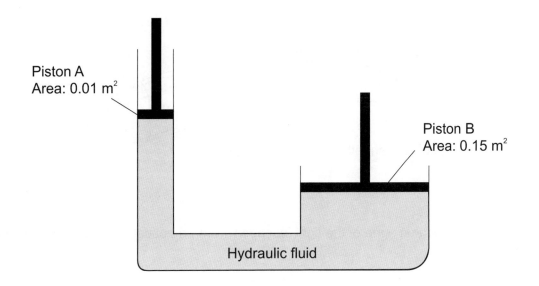

(a)   Explain why there is a force on piston B when a force is applied to piston A.

....

....

....

....

[3]

(b) (i) Show that the force on piston B is 375 N when a force of 25 N is applied to piston A.

[4]

(ii) Explain why the pressure is slightly different at piston A and piston B when the hydraulic system is in the position shown in the diagram.

....

....

[1]

[Total 8 marks]

Turn over ▶

10   Optical fibres, such as the one shown below, are used in medicine.

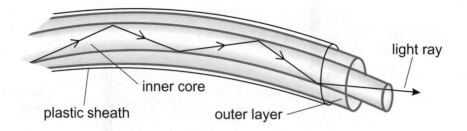

(a)   Explain why almost none of the light 'escapes' from an optical fibre as a light ray travels along it.

....

....

....

[2]

(b)   Describe an experiment to find the refractive index of a rectangular block of the material used to make optical fibres.

....

....

....

....

....

....

[4]

(c)   The refractive index of the material is 1.5. Light is shone into a semi-circular block of the same material at different angles. As shown in the diagram, an angle, θ, is reached at which the light refracts along the flat boundary between the block and the air.

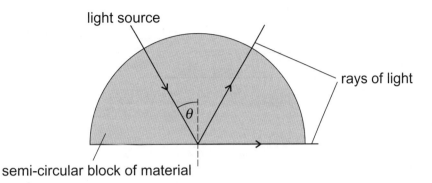

Calculate the angle θ.

θ = ... °

[4]

[Total 10 marks]

11   This question is about velocity-time graphs.

(a)   The velocity-time graph shows the motion of a vehicle as it travels along a flat, straight road before braking and stopping at a set of traffic lights.

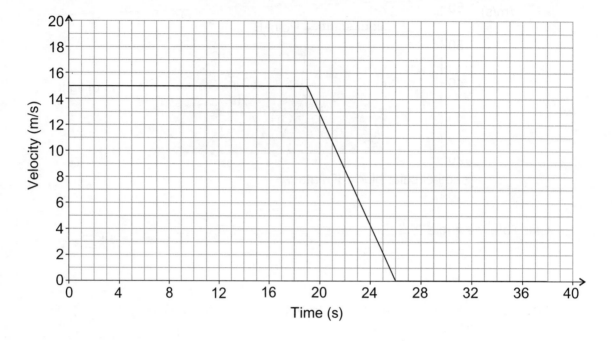

(i) Calculate the total distance travelled by the car in the first 28 seconds.

Total distance travelled = ... m

[2]

(ii) Describe what happens to the temperature of the car brakes when they are applied to slow the car down. Explain why this happens.

....

....

....

[2]

(b) This velocity-time graph shows the motion of a skydiver jumping from an aeroplane.

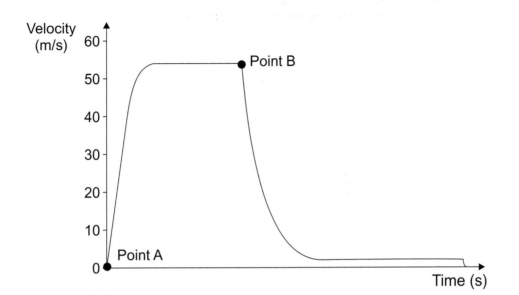

(i) Describe the motion of the skydiver from point A to point B on the graph, in terms of the forces acting on him.

....

....

....

....

....

....

[4]

(ii) At point B, the skydiver opens his parachute.
Explain why this causes the change in his velocity.

....

....

....

[2]

[Total 10 marks]

12 Pollen grains move around randomly when suspended in water, as shown in the diagram.

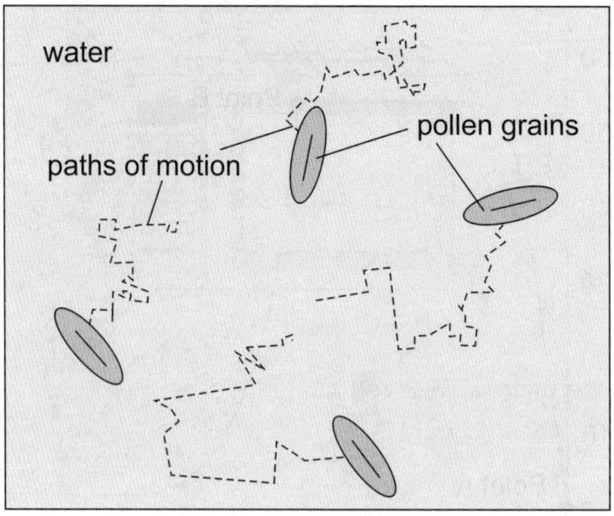

(a) State the name given to this type of motion.

....

[1]

(b) Explain what causes the pollen grains to move in this way.

....

....

....

....

....

[3]

(c) Give the name of the theory that this motion is evidence for.

....

[1]

[Total 5 marks]

13   A microwave oven can be used for heating food quickly.

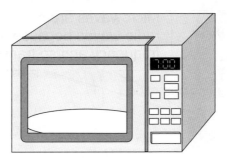

(a)   Describe how the microwave oven heats food.

....

....

....

....

[3]

(b) (i)   State the equation linking frequency, wavelength and speed.

....

[1]

(ii)   A microwave uses microwaves with a frequency of 2.5×10^9 Hz that travel at 3.0×10^8 m/s. Calculate the wavelength of these microwaves.

Wavelength = ... m

[2]

(c) (i)   Mobile phones work by transmitting and receiving microwave signals. Explain why some people are concerned about using microwaves in this way.

....

....

....

[2]

Turn over ▶

(ii) A student is discussing the dangers of microwaves and radio waves.

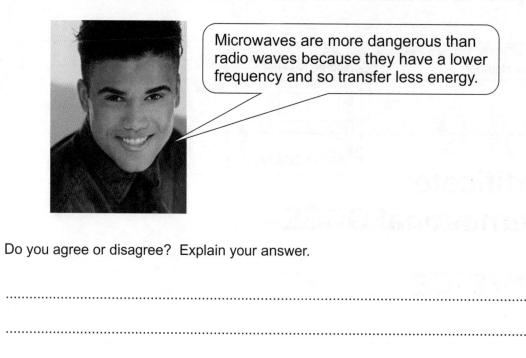

Microwaves are more dangerous than radio waves because they have a lower frequency and so transfer less energy.

Do you agree or disagree? Explain your answer.

....

....

....

[3]

d)   Give **one** other use of microwaves.

....

[1]

[Total 12 marks]

[Total for paper 120 marks]

Candidate Surname | Candidate Forename(s)

Centre Number | Candidate Number

Certificate International GCSE

Physics

Paper 2P

Practice Paper

Time allowed: 1 hour

You must have:
- A ruler.
- A calculator.

Total marks:

Instructions to candidates
- Use **black** ink to write your answers.
- Write your name and other details in the spaces provided above.
- Answer **all** questions in the spaces provided.
- In calculations, show clearly how you worked out your answers.
- You will need to answer some questions by placing a cross in a box, like this: x
  To change your answer, draw a line through the box like this: ~~x~~
  Then mark your new answer as normal.

Information for candidates
- The marks available are given in brackets at the end of each question.
- There are 60 marks available for this paper.
- You might find the equations on page 148 useful.

Advice for candidates
- Read all the questions carefully.
- Write your answers as clearly and neatly as possible.
- Keep in mind how much time you have left.

Get the answers

Your free Online Edition of this book includes the complete answers for this Exam Paper — you can even print them out. There's more info about how to get your Online Edition at the front of this book.

Answer **all** questions

1   A fire engine speeds past an observer.
     Sound waves are emitted from the fire engine's siren as it travels.

(a) (i) Which of the following describes the **amplitude** of a wave?
         Place a cross (x) in the appropriate box to indicate your answer.

         ☐   The height of the wave, from a trough to a crest.

         ☐   The length of the wave, from a crest to a crest.

         ☐   The height of the wave, from the rest position to a crest.

         ☐   The length of the wave, from a trough to a crest.

                                                                              [1]

    (ii) Which of the following describes the **frequency** of a wave?
         Place a cross (x) in the appropriate box to indicate your answer.

         ☐   The number of complete waves passing a certain point per second.

         ☐   The number of complete waves passing a certain point per minute.

         ☐   The number of crests and troughs passing a certain point per minute.

         ☐   The number of crests and troughs passing a certain point per second.

                                                                              [1]

(b)   Describe the direction of oscillations relative to the direction of energy transfer
        for a sound wave.

        ....

        ....
                                                                                                                      [1]

(c)   The siren sounds quieter as the fire engine gets further away from the observer.
        Suggest what this tells you about the amplitude of the sound waves reaching the observer.

        ....

        ....
                                                                                                                      [1]

(d)   The fire engine drives round a corner. The observer can no longer see the fire engine,
        but she can still hear its siren.

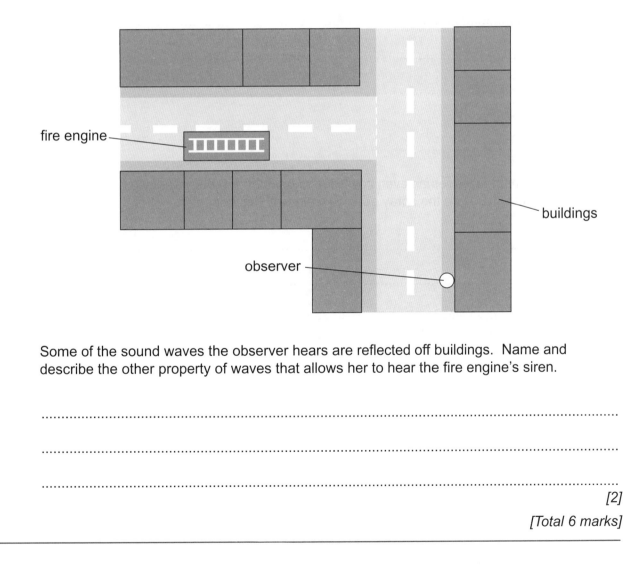

        Some of the sound waves the observer hears are reflected off buildings. Name and
        describe the other property of waves that allows her to hear the fire engine's siren.

        ....

        ....

        ....
                                                                                                                      [2]
                                                                                                      [Total 6 marks]

                                                                                              Turn over ▶

2 The body panels of a plane are painted with a spray gun that gives the paint droplets a negative static charge. The body panels are given a positive static charge.

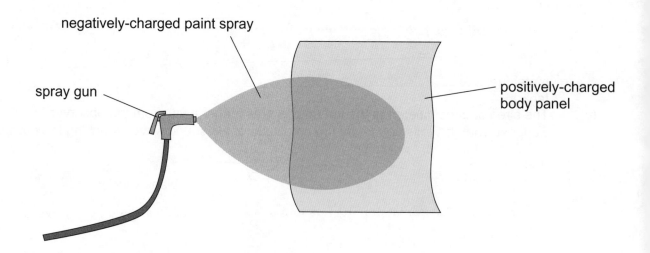

negatively-charged paint spray

spray gun

positively-charged body panel

(a) (i) Explain why the spray gun produces a fine, even spray of paint.

....

....

....

[1]

(ii) This method leaves an even coverage of paint on the body panels, including areas that are not directly facing the spray gun. Explain why this happens.

....

....

....

....

[2]

(b)   When a plane is being refuelled, fuel is pumped into a tank in the wing of the plane.
The tank and wing are made from metal, which is an electrical conductor, and connected
to earth.

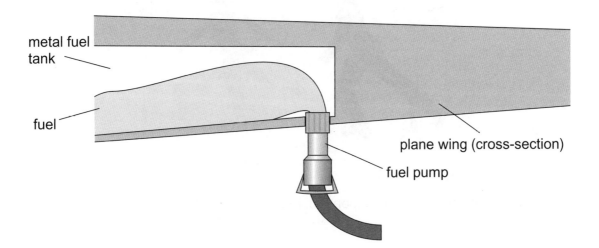

metal fuel
tank

fuel

plane wing (cross-section)

fuel pump

Describe, in terms of particle transfer, how a static charge could build up on the fuel tank
during refuelling if the tank were made from an electrical insulator. Explain why a build-up
of static charge on the fuel tank could be dangerous.

....

....

....

....

....

[3]

[Total 6 marks]

Turn over ▶

3   Two skaters are taking part in a figure skating contest.
The diagram below shows their velocity and mass at one point in their routine.

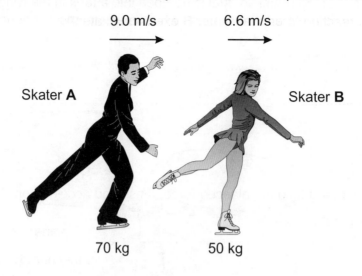

9.0 m/s   6.6 m/s

Skater **A**   Skater **B**

70 kg   50 kg

(a)   State the equation linking momentum, mass and velocity.

....

[1]

(b)   Complete the table below to show the momentum of each skater.

	Mass (kg)	Velocity (m/s to the right)	Momentum (kg m/s to the right)
Skater A	70	9.0	....
Skater B	50	6.6	....

[2]

(c)   The skaters continue at the same velocity until Skater A catches up with skater B and holds on to her. They continue to move in the same direction.

Calculate their velocity immediately after skater A begins to hold skater B.

Velocity = ... m/s

[2]

(d)   During the routine, the skaters come to a stop. Skater A then pushes skater B away from him with a force of 100 N.

(i)   Describe the reaction force that skater B exerts on skater A.

....

....

[1]

(ii) State the equation linking unbalanced force, mass and acceleration.

....

[1]

(iii) Calculate skater B's acceleration due to this force and state the correct unit. Assume there are no frictional forces acting on her.

Acceleration = ... unit ....

[3]

[Total 10 marks]

4 The pie chart shows the proportions of a country's electricity generated by different resources.

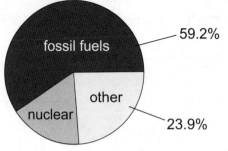

fossil fuels

59.2%

other

nuclear

23.9%

(a) Calculate the proportion of the country's electricity that comes from nuclear power.

Proportion from nuclear power = ...%

[1]

(b) Describe the advantages and disadvantages of using nuclear power to generate electricity compared to burning fossil fuels.

....

....

....

....

....

[4]

(c) Nuclear fuel emits ionising radiation and precautions must be taken while handling it.

(i) Describe the damage that can be done by ionising radiation to living organisms.

....

....

....

[2]

(ii) Suggest **one** precaution workers in nuclear power stations could take when handling sources of ionising radiation to minimise the risk to their health.

....

....

[1]

[Total 8 marks]

5 The volume of a fixed mass of gas depends on its pressure and temperature.

(a) A student performs an experiment to show how the volume and pressure of a gas are related. She takes several readings of the volume of a fixed mass of gas at different pressures, making sure the temperature of the gas is kept constant. Her results are shown in the table below.

Pressure (kPa)	Volume (cm³)
10	5.0
20	4.0
30	3.3
40	2.8
50	0.6
60	2.0
70	1.8

(i) Name **one** control variable in the student's experiment.

....

[1]

(ii) Explain why control variables need to be kept constant in experiments such as this.

....

....

[1]

(b) (i) Use the grid to plot a graph of the results in the table.
Draw a curved line of best fit.

[5]

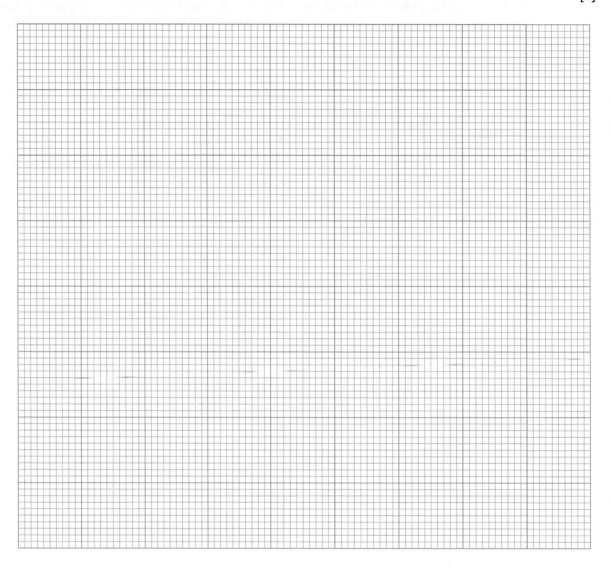

(ii) One of the results in the experiment is anomalous. Circle this result on the graph.

[1]

(iii) Using the graph, describe the relationship between the pressure and volume
of the gas at a constant temperature.

[1]

(c) The graph shows how the volume of a gas is affected by changes in temperature, at a constant pressure.

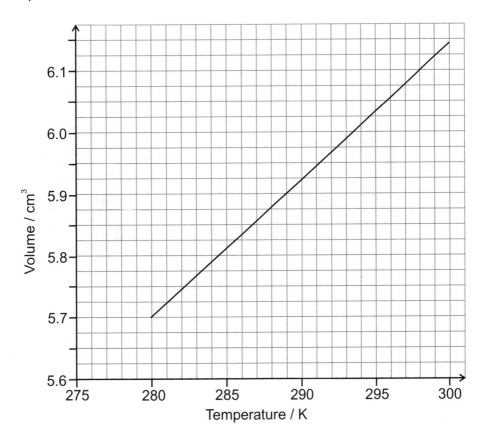

(i) Using the graph, describe the relationship between the temperature and volume of the gas at a constant pressure.

....

....

[1]

(ii) Use the graph to estimate the volume of the gas at 25 °C.

Volume of gas = ... cm³

[2]

[Total 12 marks]

Turn over ▶

Practice Paper 2P

6   The generator in a power station produces an alternating voltage of 25 kV.
This is changed to 400 kV by the transformer shown.

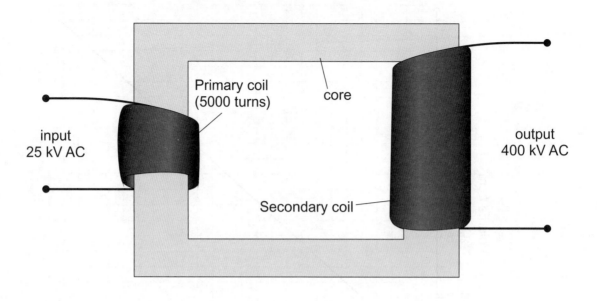

(a)   What type of transformer is shown in the diagram?
Place a cross (x) in the appropriate box to indicate your answer.

☐ Step-left transformer

☐ Step-up transformer

☐ Step-right transformer

☐ Step-down transformer

[1]

(b) (i) State the equation linking the number of turns on the primary coil, the number of turns on the secondary coil, the input voltage and the output voltage for a transformer.

....

[1]

(ii) The primary coil has 5000 turns.
Calculate the number of turns on the secondary coil.

Number of turns = ...

[3]

(c) (i) State the equation linking the input power and the output power in terms of the current and voltage across each coil of a 100% efficient transformer.

....
[1]

(ii) The output current of this transformer is 250 A.
Calculate the input current, assuming the transformer is 100% efficient.

Input current = ... A
[2]

(d) Explain how transformers are used to reduce energy loss from the cables that make up the National Grid, while ensuring that consumers are supplied with electricity at a useful and relatively safe voltage.

....

....

....

....
[3]
[Total 11 marks]

Turn over ▶

7   A construction worker is using a crane with an electromagnet to pick up a metal load.

(a)   What is an electromagnet?

....

....

[1]

(b)   The electromagnet is shown in the diagram.

(i)   Sketch magnetic field lines to show the magnetic field around the electromagnet.

[1]

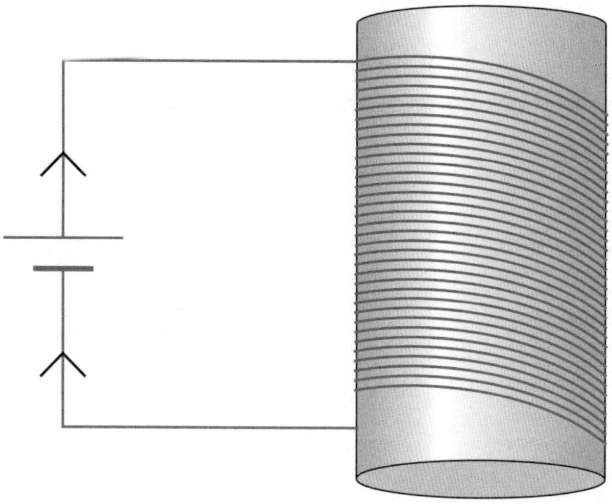

(ii) Explain why it is important for the core to be made from a magnetically soft material.

....

....

[1]

(c)   The diagram shows all the forces acting on the crane as it carries a metal anvil.

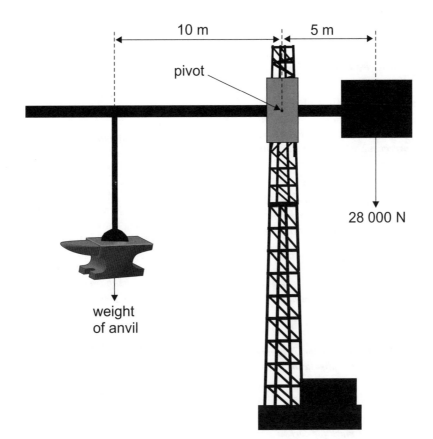

(i)   State the equation linking the moment of a force, the force and the perpendicular distance from the line of action of the force to the pivot.

....

[1]

(ii)   Use the information on the diagram to calculate the weight of the anvil if the system is balanced.

Weight = ... N

[3]

[Total 7 marks]

[Total for paper 60 marks]

/ Acceleration

$$\frac{\text{distance moved}}{\text{time taken}} \ (s = \frac{d}{t}) \ \textit{[1 mark]}$$

$$= \frac{1500}{300} = \textbf{5 m/s}$$

swer correct, otherwise 1 mark for correct
of values into the equation.]

c) $a = \frac{v - u}{t} \Rightarrow t = \frac{v - u}{a} = \frac{10 - 2}{2.4} = \textbf{3.3 s (to 2 s.f.)}$

[4 marks if answer correct, otherwise 1 mark for using the correct equation, 1 mark for correct rearrangement of the equation and 1 mark for correct substitution of values into the equation.]

2 a) $s = \frac{d}{t} \Rightarrow d = s \times t = 0.46 \times 2.4 = \textbf{1.1 m (to 2 s.f.)}$

[3 marks if answer correct, otherwise 1 mark for using the correct equation and 1 mark for correct rearrangement of the equation and correct substitution of values into the equation.]

b)   acceleration = $\frac{\text{change in velocity}}{\text{time taken}} = \frac{78.4}{8.0} = \textbf{9.8 m/s}^2$

[3 marks if answer correct, otherwise 1 mark for using the correct equation and 1 mark for correct substitution of values into the equation.]

3 a) $a = \frac{v - u}{t} = \frac{20}{3.5} = \textbf{5.7 m/s}^2 \textbf{ (to 2 s.f.)}$

[3 marks if answer correct, otherwise 1 mark for using the correct equation and 1 mark for correct substitution of values into the equation.]

b) $a = \frac{v - u}{t} \Rightarrow v = (a \times t) + u = (5.7 \times 1.5) + 0 = \textbf{8.55 m/s}$

[3 marks if answer correct, otherwise 1 mark for correct rearrangement of the equation and 1 mark for correct substitution of values into the equation.]

4 a) $a = \frac{v - u}{t} \Rightarrow u = v - (a \times t) = 5 - (3 \times 1.2)$
$$= \textbf{1.4 m/s}$$

[4 marks if answer correct, otherwise 1 mark for using the correct equation, 1 mark for correct rearrangement of the equation and 1 mark for correct substitution of values into the equation.]

b)   Yes — the tractor has changed direction, so there has been a change in velocity (and so there must have been an acceleration) *[1 mark]*.

Pages 5-6: D-T and V-T Graphs

1 a)   300 s *[1 mark]*

b)   Yes — the gradient of the graph shows the student's speed *[1 mark]* and the gradient for this part of the journey is constant (it's a straight line) *[1 mark]*.

c)   average speed = $\frac{\text{distance moved}}{\text{time taken}} = \frac{450}{300} = \textbf{1.5 m/s}$

[3 marks if answer correct, otherwise 1 mark for using the correct equation and 1 mark for correct substitution of values in the equation.]

d) E.g.

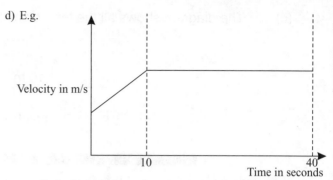

[3 marks available — 1 mark for a straight, sloped line showing the initial acceleration, 1 mark for a straight horizontal line showing the constant speed, and 1 mark for plotting a horizontal line for roughly 3 times the time the sloped line is plotted over.]

2 a) i)   Travelling at a steady velocity (20 m/s) *[1 mark]*.
    ii)   E.g. Slowing down / (increasing) deceleration *[1 mark]*.

b)   Distance travelled = area under graph
$$= (60 - 40) \times (20 - 0)$$
$$= \textbf{400 m}$$

[3 marks for the correct answer, otherwise 1 mark for attempting to find the area under the graph between 40 and 60 seconds, 1 mark for correctly showing (60 − 40) × 20 or 20 × 20.]

c)   Acceleration = gradient = $\frac{20 - 0}{40 - 0} = \textbf{0.5 m/s}^2$

[3 marks for the correct answer, otherwise 1 mark for attempting to find the gradient, 1 mark for dividing a correct change in velocity by a correct change in time in the time range 0 – 40 s.]

d)   Velocity in m/s

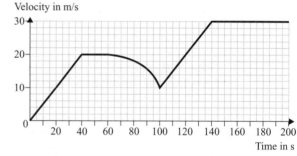

[1 mark for a straight line with a positive gradient between 100 and 140 seconds, 1 mark for a straight horizontal line between 140 and 200 seconds.]

Page 7: Mass, Weight and Gravity

1 a) i)   Weight = mass × gravitational field strength ($W = m \times g$) *[1 mark]*

    ii) $W = m \times g \Rightarrow g = \frac{W}{m} = \frac{19.6}{2}$
$$= \textbf{9.8 newtons per kilogram (N/kg)}$$

[3 marks if answer correct, otherwise 1 mark for correct rearrangement of the equation and correct substitution of values into the equation, and 1 mark for correct unit. Allow m/s² as a correct unit.]

b)   The weight would be smaller *[1 mark]* as the gravitational field strength, g, is lower on the moon *[1 mark]*.

Page 8: Forces and Friction

1 a)   gravitational *[1 mark]*

b)   frictional *[1 mark]*, electrostatic *[1 mark]*, newtons *[1 mark]*

131

2 a) i)

[1 mark for labelled arrow pointing backwards.]

ii) As the speed increases, the drag force increases *[1 mark]*.

b) Any one of e.g.:

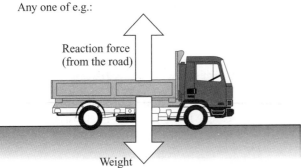

[1 mark for force label and 1 mark for direction.]

You could write "gravitational force" instead of "weight" here.

Page 9: Investigating Motion

1 a) i)

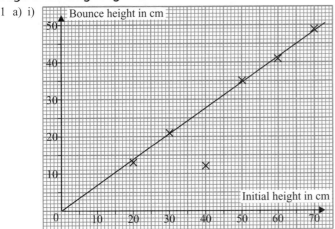

[5 marks available — 1 mark for choosing a suitable scale (using at least half of the grid), 1 mark for correctly labelled axes, 1 mark for plotting at least 5 points correctly to the nearest half square, 1 further mark for plotting all 6 points correctly, and 1 mark for an appropriate line of best fit that ignores the anomalous result at (40, 12).]

Graphs are a great place to pick up a load of marks, which means they're also a great place to lose loads of marks if you're not careful. Make sure you use a sharp pencil and a transparent ruler, and try to have to same number of points above and below your line of best fit.

ii) As the initial height increases, the bounce height increases / they're (directly) proportional *[1 mark]*.

b) E.g. drop the ball from a fixed height *[1 mark]* and measure the height of each successive bounce *[1 mark]*.

Pages 10-11: Terminal Velocity

1 a) Dirk is not correct. There are actually multiple forces acting on the object *[1 mark]*, but the forces in each direction are balanced *[1 mark]*.

If you answered Jenny, you receive no marks for this question regardless of the reasoning.

b) When an object falls, resistive forces (e.g. air resistance) act on it in the opposite direction to its motion *[1 mark]*. Eventually these balance the downward force of an object's weight *[1 mark]*.

c) The ball with the lower weight. Air resistance increases with velocity *[1 mark]*, and the air resistance at any given velocity will be the same on each ball (because they're the same size) *[1 mark]*. So air resistance will balance the lower-weight ball's weight at a lower velocity, giving a lower terminal velocity *[1 mark]*.

If you answered the ball with the larger mass, you receive no marks for this question regardless of the reasoning.

2 a) i) This will ensure the weight and shape of the ball remain constant *[1 mark]*, so the only thing affecting the rate at which it falls is the parachute *[1 mark]*.

ii) Any one of, e.g.:
Dropping the ball from as large a height as possible *[1 mark]* to allow time to prepare for stopping the timer and to reduce uncertainty in the time reading *[1 mark]*. / Using parachutes with a much smaller mass than the steel ball *[1 mark]* so changing the parachute has little effect on the total mass *[1 mark]*. / Repeating each reading 3 (or more) times and calculating an average *[1 mark]* to reduce the chance of random errors or anomalous results affecting the outcome *[1 mark]*.

There are loads of possible answers you could give here — just make sure you answer the question properly and you explain your answer well.

b) i) slowly *[1 mark]*
ii) larger *[1 mark]*

c) E.g. repeating the experiment with steel balls with different masses *[1 mark]* and using the same parachute throughout *[1 mark]*.

You get one mark here for describing a way of changing the mass and one mark for describing how you'd control an independent variable that isn't being tested.

Pages 12-13: The Three Laws of Motion

1 balanced *[1 mark]*, accelerates *[1 mark]*, force *[1 mark]*

2 a) $F = m \times a$ *[1 mark]*
For the Heath TT:
$F = m \times a = 950 \times 3 = 2850$ N *[1 mark]*
For the Asquith 380:
$F = m \times a = 790 \times 2 = 1580$ N *[1 mark]*
So the Heath TT has a greater maximum driving force.

b) **800 kg** *[1 mark]*

This is calculated by rearranging $F = m \times a$ to get $\frac{F}{a} = \frac{4000}{5} = 800$.

3 a) $F = m \times a \Rightarrow a = \frac{F}{m} = \frac{200}{2500} = $ **0.08 m/s²**
[3 marks if answer correct, otherwise 1 mark for using the correct equation, and 1 mark for correct rearrangement of the equation and correct substitution of values into the equation.]

b) i) $F = m \times a = 10 \times 29 = $ **290 N**
[2 marks if answer correct, otherwise 1 mark for correct substitution of values into the equation.]

ii) Force exerted on the van by the traffic cone = **290 N** *[1 mark]*

iii) Assuming all of this force causes the van to decelerate:
$F = m \times a \Rightarrow a = \frac{F}{m} = \frac{290}{2500} = $ **0.116 m/s²**
[2 marks if answer correct, otherwise 1 mark for correct rearrangement of the equation and correct substitution of values into the equation.]

4 a) force = mass × acceleration ($F = m \times a$) *[1 mark]*

b) The maximum force of the engine in each scooter (= $m \times a$)
= 127.5 × 2.4 *[1 mark]*
= 306 N *[1 mark]*
So, the mass of student B and her scooter = $\frac{F}{a}$
= $\frac{306}{1.70}$ *[1 mark]*
= **180 kg** *[1 mark]*

Page 14: Combining Forces

1 a) A scalar quantity just has size (magnitude) / is just a number *[1 mark]*. A vector quantity also has a direction *[1 mark]*.

b) force *[1 mark]*

c) 14 kg *[1 mark]*

2 a) Resultant force in the horizontal direction:
$17 + 3 - 10 - 10 = 0$ N
Resultant force in the vertical direction:
$10 - 2 = $ **8 N** *[1 mark]* **up** *[1 mark]*

b) i) $y - 4 = 0 \Rightarrow y = $ **4** *[1 mark]*

ii) $20 - 5 - x = 0 \Rightarrow x = 20 - 5 = $ **15 N** *[1 mark]*

Page 15: Stopping Distances

1 a) i) Thinking distance *[1 mark]*.

ii) Any two from e.g.:
tiredness / speed of the car / drug or alcohol intake / inexperience.
[2 marks available — 1 mark for each correct answer.]

b) i) Braking distance *[1 mark]*.

ii) Any two from e.g.:
speed of the car / mass of the car / condition of the car's brakes / condition of the road surface / condition of the car's tyres.
[2 marks available — 1 mark for each correct answer.]

2 a) E.g. Rain makes the road slippy and reduces friction between the tyres and the road *[1 mark]*, increasing the braking distance *[1 mark]*.

b) E.g. Decrease her speed *[1 mark]*

Pages 16-17: Momentum and Collisions

1 a) i) momentum = mass × velocity ($p = m \times v$) *[1 mark]*

ii) $p = m \times v = 1200 \times 30$
= **36 000 kilogram metres per second (kg m/s)**
[3 marks if answer correct, otherwise 1 mark for correct substitution of values into the equation and 1 mark for correct unit.]

b) i) force = $\dfrac{\text{change in momentum}}{\text{time taken}}$ *[1 mark]*

ii) force = $\dfrac{\text{change in momentum}}{\text{time taken}} = \dfrac{36\,000}{1.2} = $ **30 000 N**
[2 marks if answer correct, otherwise 1 mark for correct substitution of values into the equation. Allow full marks if an incorrect answer from part a) is used and the calculations are done correctly.]

2 initial momentum of skater = $60 \times 5 = 300$ kg m/s
momentum of skater and bag = $(60 + \text{mass}_{\text{bag}}) \times 4.8$
momentum before = momentum after
$\Rightarrow 300 = (60 + \text{mass}_{\text{bag}}) \times 4.8$
$\Rightarrow \text{mass}_{\text{bag}} = \dfrac{300}{4.8} - 60 = $ **2.5 kg**
[5 marks if answer correct, otherwise 1 mark for reference to equal momentum before and after, 1 mark for correct substitution of values to calculate the initial momentum of the skater, 1 mark for correct rearrangement of the equation and 1 mark for correct substitution of values into the equations for momentum of the skater and momentum of the skater and bag.]

3 a) $p = m \times v = 650 \times 15$
= **9750 kilogram metres per second (kg m/s)**
[4 marks if answer correct, otherwise 1 mark for using the correct equation, 1 mark for correct substitution of values into the equation and 1 mark for correct unit.]

b) momentum before = momentum after
$[m_1 \times v_1] + [m_2 \times v_2] = [(650 + 750) \times v_{\text{after}}]$
$[650 \times 15] + [750 \times -10] = [(650 + 750) \times v_{\text{after}}]$
$9750 - 7500 = 1400 \times v_{\text{after}}$
$v_{\text{after}} = \dfrac{2250}{1400}$
$v_{\text{after}} = $ **1.6 m/s (to 2 s.f.)**
[4 marks if answer correct, otherwise 1 mark for equating momentum before and after, 1 mark for correct substitution of values into the equations for momentum of each vehicle and 1 mark for correct rearrangement of the equation(s). Allow full marks if an incorrect answer from part a) is used and the calculations are done correctly.]

c) The crumple zone increases the time taken by the car to stop/change its velocity *[1 mark]*. The time over which momentum changes is inversely proportional to the force acting, so this reduces the force *[1 mark]*.

Page 18: Turning Forces and Centre of Gravity

1 a) B *[1 mark]*— the force is at the furthest distance from the pivot and is acting in a direction perpendicular to the handle *[1 mark]*.

b) i) force *[1 mark]*

ii) gravity *[1 mark]*

c) i) moment = force × perpendicular distance from the line of action of the force to the pivot ($M = F \times d$) *[1 mark]*

ii) $M = F \times d = 45 \times 0.1 = $ **4.5 newton metres (Nm)**
[3 marks if answer correct, otherwise 1 mark for correct unit and 1 mark for correct substitution of values into the equation.]

Page 19: Principle of Moments

1 a) moment = force × perpendicular distance from the pivot
$= 2 \times 0.2 = $ **0.4 Nm**
[3 marks if answer correct, otherwise 1 mark for using the correct equation and 1 mark for correct substitution of values into the equation.]

b) clockwise moments about pivot = anticlockwise moments about pivot
$\text{force}_C \times \text{perpendicular distance}_C = 0.4 + 0.8$
$\text{perpendicular distance}_C = \dfrac{0.4 + 0.8}{8} = $ **0.15 m**
[4 marks if answer correct, otherwise 1 mark for reference to balanced moments in each direction, 1 mark for correct substitution of values into the equation and 1 mark for correct rearrangement of the equation. Allow full marks if an incorrect answer from part a) is used and the calculations are done correctly.]

2 Situation B. Rope 1 balances the moment applied by the box around rope 2 *[1 mark]* and so the further the box is from rope 2, the larger the force applied by rope 1 *[1 mark]*.
Award no marks for this question if you answered situation A.

Page 20: Hooke's Law

1 a) Any two from, e.g. fixing the ruler with a clamp and marking the zero position of the end of the rope on the ruler / repeating each measurement at least three times and calculating averages / adding a separate marker to the show the top of the rope (to ensure it is at the same point each time). *[2 marks — one for each correct answer.]*

b) shape / length / size *[1 mark]*, proportional *[1 mark]*, elastic *[1 mark]*.

There are quite a few things you could write for the first word — as long as your answer seems sensible give yourself the mark.

Page 21: Gravity and the Universe

1 a) a collection of billions of stars. *[1 mark]*
  b) the Sun. *[1 mark]*
  c) billions of galaxies. *[1 mark]*
2 a) The Milky Way *[1 mark]*.
  b) (Roughly) circular *[1 mark]*.
  c) Satellite(s) *[1 mark]*, the gravitational force *[1 mark]*.

Pages 22-23: Orbital Speed

1 a) C *[1 mark]* — Comets usually have (highly) elliptical orbits *[1 mark]*.
  b) i) slightly elliptical *[1 mark]*.
    ii) much longer that Earth's. *[1 mark]*
    iii) 1.2 km/s — orbital speed only depends on the orbital radius and the time period.
    [1 mark for the correct speed and the correct reason.]
  c) $\text{orbital speed} = \dfrac{2 \times \pi \times \text{orbital radius}}{\text{time period}}$

  $= \dfrac{2 \times \pi \times 42\,000\,000}{(24 \times 60 \times 60)}$

  **= 3100 metres per second (m/s)
  or 3.1 kilometres per second (km/s) (to 2 s.f.)**
  [3 marks if answer correct, otherwise 1 mark for correct substitution of values into the equation and 1 mark for correct unit.]
2 a) $72 \times 365 \times 24 \times 60 \times 60 = \mathbf{2.27 \times 10^9}$ **s (to 3 s.f.)** *[1 mark]*
  There are 365 days in a year, 24 hours in a day, 60 minutes in an hour and 60 seconds in a minute — that's where all these numbers come from.
  b) At the point where the comet is at its closest point to the Sun *[1 mark]* because that's where the Sun's gravitational force is strongest *[1 mark]*.
  c) $\text{orbital speed} = \dfrac{2 \times \pi \times \text{orbital radius}}{\text{time period}}$

  $\Rightarrow \text{orbital radius} = \dfrac{\text{orbital speed} \times \text{time period}}{2 \times \pi}$

  $= \dfrac{48\,000 \times (2.27 \times 10^9)}{2 \times \pi}$

  $= \mathbf{1.74 \times 10^{13}}$ **m (to 3 s.f.)**
  [3 marks if answer correct, otherwise 1 mark for correct rearrangement of the equation and 1 mark for correct substitution of values into the equation.]

Section 2 — Electricity

Page 24: Safe Plugs

1 a) Any two of: One of the plugs has a cracked casing *[1 mark]* which could expose live parts and give someone a shock if they touched them *[1 mark]*. / One cable is frayed *[1 mark]*, which could expose live parts and give someone a shock if they touched them *[1 mark]*. / One cable is very long and trailing on the floor *[1 mark]*. This could be a trip hazard *[1 mark]*. / There is water close to plug sockets/plug cables *[1 mark]*, which is dangerous as water can conduct electricity *[1 mark]*. / There is a child pushing a metal object into a plug socket *[1 mark]*, which is unsafe as metal conducts electricity and the child could get an electric shock *[1 mark]*.
  b) i) The kettle is double insulated. / Plastic is an (electrical) insulator *[1 mark]*. This means the casing doesn't conduct electricity, so it can never become live *[1 mark]*.
    ii) Disagree. When the toaster is working properly, no current should be flowing in the earth wire *[1 mark]*.
  c) Any one of: Plug pins / fuse holder / wires / wire attachments *[1 mark]*. Reason — because brass/copper/metals are good conductors of electricity *[1 mark]*.

Page 25: Fuses and Circuit Breakers

1 a) i) The metal casing can become live and give someone an electric shock if they touch it *[1 mark]*.
    ii) A large current surges to earth through the earth wire *[1 mark]*. This causes a large current to surge through the live wire and trip the circuit breaker *[1 mark]*. The circuit breaker breaks the circuit and isolates the microwave *[1 mark]*.
  b) i) A fuse melts to break a circuit *[1 mark]* whereas a circuit breaker opens a switch to break a circuit *[1 mark]*.
    ii) Any two of: Circuit breakers don't need to be replaced every time they break the circuit/can be easily reset. / Some circuit breakers operate much faster than a fuse, making them safer. / Some circuit breakers can detect and respond to much smaller (but still dangerous) current changes than a fuse. *[2 marks — 1 mark for each correct advantage.]*

Pages 26-27: Energy and Power in Circuits

1 a) i) So that when the current flows through the wire it gets hot (and so can be used to heat the water in the kettle) *[1 mark]*.
    ii) As the element gets hotter, the resistance of the element will increase *[1 mark]*.
  b) i) Power = current × voltage or $P = I \times V$
    [1 mark — accept any rearranged version of the same equation.]
    ii) $I = \dfrac{P}{V} = \dfrac{2.8 \times 1000}{230} = 12.17... \text{A} = \mathbf{12}$ **amps (A) (to 2 s.f.)**
    [3 marks available for correct answer, otherwise 1 mark for correctly substituting into a correctly rearranged equation and 1 mark for giving the correct unit.]
    iii) 13 A *[1 mark]*
  Remember that fuses should be rated as near as possible but just higher than the normal operating current, which is 12 A here.
    iv) She should choose kettle B because it has the higher power rating *[1 mark]*. This means that it transfers more energy (to heat energy) per unit time, so it will boil the water faster *[1 mark]*.
2 a) $E = I \times V \times t$ so $t = \dfrac{E}{I \times V} = \dfrac{828}{2.3 \times 12} = \mathbf{30}$ **s**
  [3 marks for correct answer, otherwise 1 mark for rearranging the equation and 1 mark for correctly substituting into the equation.]
  b) Disagree. The fuse should be rated as close as possible but just above the normal operating current *[1 mark]*. If the fuse is below the normal operating current it will blow straight away even if there is no fault *[1 mark]*.
3 a) Power = **23 (W)** *[1 mark]*
  and energy transferred in 1 minute = **1380 (J)** *[1 mark]*
  $P = I \times V = 0.1 \times 230 = 23$ (W)
  $E = I \times V \times t = 0.1 \times 230 \times 60 = 1380$ (J)
  b) Lamp A *[1 mark — if answer to 3 a) was incorrect and higher than 1800 J, allow this mark for saying lamp C.]*

136

Page 28: Circuits — the Basics

1 a) volts *[1 mark]*, alternating *[1 mark]*, e.g. changes direction/alternates *[1 mark]*.

   b) direct current (d.c.) *[1 mark]*.

2 a)

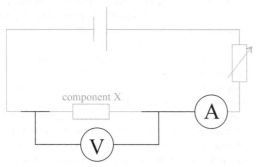

   [2 marks available — 1 mark for adding the ammeter in line with component X, 1 mark for adding the voltmeter across component X]

   b) It will decrease *[1 mark]*.

   c) E.g. Start with the resistance of the variable resistor fixed at a high level *[1 mark]*, then take a reading of current from the ammeter *[1 mark]* and voltage from the voltmeter *[1 mark]*. Decrease the resistance of the variable resistor in equal steps and take another pair of readings each time *[1 mark]*. Make sure you take several pairs of readings *[1 mark]*.

With these sort of questions, you just need to make sure you get all the key points down. You could pick up some of the marks for saying things like you'll take repeats of all your readings and take averages, or for describing how you'll make it a fair test.

Pages 29-30: Resistance and V = I × R

1 a) resistor *[1 mark]*

   b) (component) D *[1 mark]*

The graph with the shallowest gradient corresponds to the component with the highest resistance.

   c) i) Gradient $= \dfrac{\text{vertical change}}{\text{horizontal change}} = \dfrac{\text{current}}{\text{voltage}} = \dfrac{4}{2} = 2$

   [2 marks available for correct answer, otherwise 1 mark for showing that the gradient is the vertical change divided by the horizontal change.]

   ii) Voltage = current × resistance or $V = I \times R$
   [1 mark — accept any rearranged version of the same equation.]

   iii) $g = \dfrac{I}{V}$ *[1 mark]*. $V = I \times R$ so $R = \dfrac{V}{I}$ so $R = \dfrac{1}{g}$ *[1 mark]*

   iv) $R = \dfrac{1}{g} = \dfrac{1}{2} = 0.5\ \Omega$
   [2 marks for correct answer, otherwise 1 mark for correctly substituting into the equation.]

   v) $V = I \times R$ so $I = \dfrac{V}{R} = \dfrac{15}{0.75} = 20\ \text{A}$
   [2 marks for correct answer, otherwise 1 mark for correctly substituting into the correct rearranged equation.]

2 a) diode *[1 mark]*
   current only flows in one direction *[1 mark]*.

   b)

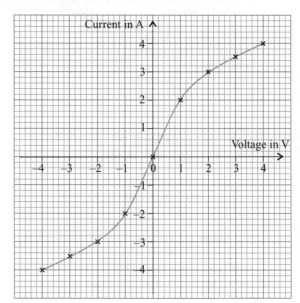

   [5 marks available — 1 mark for a suitable scale chosen (more than half of the graph paper is used), 1 mark for a suitable line of best fit passing through (0, 0), 1 mark for the axes correctly labelled with quantities and units, 2 marks for all the points plotted correctly to within half a square, or 1 mark if only one point is plotted incorrectly.]

   c) i) (filament) lamp / bulb *[1 mark]*

   ii) As the current through the filament of the lamp increases, the temperature increases. *[1 mark]* The temperature increase causes the resistance to increase *[1 mark]*. Resistance is equal to 1 ÷ gradient, so the gradient decreases, causing the graph to curve *[1 mark]*.

Page 31: LDRs, Thermistors and LEDs

1 a) i) ⊢▭⊣ *[1 mark]*

   ii) ⊶ ⊷ *[1 mark]*

   b) i) E.g.

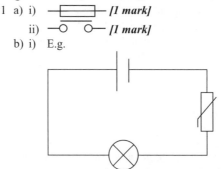

   [3 marks available for a circuit diagram showing a circuit that will work containing a thermistor, a power source and a lamp, otherwise 1 mark for an incorrect but complete circuit containing 3 components including a lamp, 1 mark for drawing a thermistor in a complete circuit.]

   ii) The current increases *[1 mark]*. As the temperature in the room increases, the resistance of the thermistor (and so the circuit) will decrease *[1 mark]*.

2 a) If the LED is lit up, current is flowing in the circuit *[1 mark]*.

   b) i) E.g. any of: Both have a resistance that varies *[1 mark]*. / Both are affected by external conditions *[1 mark]*.

   ii) E.g. Thermistors are affected by temperature whereas LDRs are affected by light intensity *[1 mark]*.

Page 32: Series and Parallel Circuits

1 a) i) E.g. if one fairy light breaks, the rest still light up *[1 mark]*.
   ii) $V = I \times R$ *[1 mark]*

$$R = \frac{V}{I} = \frac{12}{0.5} = 24\ \Omega$$

[2 marks for correct answer, otherwise 1 mark for correct substitution.]
   iii) It would increase *[1 mark]*.
  b) The windscreen wipers, headlights and air conditioning must all be wired in parallel *[1 mark]*.

Page 33: Charge, Voltage and Energy Change

1 a) i) Rate of flow of charge *[1 mark]*.
   ii) It is carried by negatively charged electrons *[1 mark]*.
  b) i) Charge = current × time or $Q = I \times t$
[1 mark — accept any rearranged version of the same equation.]
   ii) $Q = I \times t = 5 \times (20 \times 60) = $ **6000 coulombs (C)**
[4 marks for correct answer, otherwise 1 mark for calculating the time in seconds, 1 mark for correctly substituting and 1 mark for the correct unit.]
   iii) The current will be double the original current (i.e. 10 A) *[1 mark]*.
  c) Energy transferred per unit charge is also known as voltage. The battery has a voltage of 3 V or 3 J/C, so 3 J of energy is transferred by the battery per coulomb.
[3 marks available — 1 mark for saying that voltage in V is energy transferred per coulomb, 1 mark for getting 3 and 1 mark for the correct units.]

Pages 34-35: Static Electricity

1 a) A material that doesn't conduct charge/electricity very well *[1 mark]*.
  b) Plastic: No, Yes *[1 mark]*
    Copper: Yes, No *[1 mark]*
2 a) When the cloth duster and the balloon are rubbed together, the friction causes electrons to be transferred *[1 mark]* from the balloon to the cloth *[1 mark]*.
  b) E.g. any of: Use a gold leaf electroscope *[1 mark]*. Hold the balloon close to the metal disc of the electroscope. If the balloon is charged the gold leaves will become charged and repel each other, causing them to rise *[1 mark]*. / Use a rod with a known charge *[1 mark]*. Bring it close to the balloon and look for attraction or repulsion *[1 mark]*.
  c) −1.5 µC *[1 mark]*. The same number of electrons that were lost by the balloon were gained by the cloth, so it should have an equal but opposite charge to the balloon *[1 mark]*.
3 a) Rubber is an insulator *[1 mark]* so the positive charge can't move and the belt stays positively charged until it meets the top comb/the dome cannot discharge through the belt *[1 mark]*.
  b) It needs to conduct charge so that the positive charge it gets from the rubber is transferred to the metal dome *[1 mark]*.
  c) The belt is positively charged and electrons are negatively charged and opposite charges attract *[1 mark]*.
  d) The pieces of paper become positively charged when they touch the dome *[1 mark]*. They then have the same charge as the dome (and each other) and so are repelled by the dome, which makes them 'jump' *[1 mark]*.

Pages 36-37: Static Electricity — Examples

1 a) Inside the printer are two metal plates that can have a voltage applied to them *[1 mark]*. The voltage gives the plates opposite charges, which causes the droplets passing between them to be deflected, as they are attracted by one and repelled by the other *[1 mark]*. The amount and direction of deflection can be controlled by changing the size and direction of the voltage *[1 mark]*.
  b) i) Light reflected off some parts (the white parts) of the original document onto the image plate *[1 mark]*.
   ii) The black parts of the document don't reflect light onto the plate, so the image plate keeps its positive charge in those places *[1 mark]*. A negatively-charged black powder *[1 mark]* is brought close to the plate and attracted to the positively-charged parts of it *[1 mark]*. Then a positively-charged piece of paper *[1 mark]* is brought close to the plate and the negatively-charged black powder is attracted to the paper *[1 mark]*.
2 a) Rain drops and ice bumping together in clouds causes electrons to be transferred, causing the top and bottom layers of the cloud to become (oppositely) charged *[1 mark]*. This causes a big voltage between different parts of the cloud / between the (bottom of the) cloud and earth which may discharge through a spark (lightning) *[1 mark]*.
3 a) It can cause a discharge spark *[1 mark]*, which can cause a fire or an explosion if it ignites fuel or fuel fumes *[1 mark]*.
  b) E.g. Make the nozzle out of metal *[1 mark]*.
Connect the fuel nozzle to the fuel tank with an earthing strap *[1 mark]*.

Section 3 — Waves

Pages 38-39: Waves — The Basics

1 a) energy *[1 mark]*, information *[1 mark]*, matter *[1 mark]* or information *[1 mark]*, energy *[1 mark]*, matter *[1 mark]*.
  b) i) Type B is a transverse wave, because the vibrations are perpendicular to the direction of energy transfer *[1 mark]*.
   ii) Type A vibrates in the same direction as/parallel to the direction of energy transfer *[1 mark]*. Type B vibrates at 90°/ perpendicular to the direction of energy transfer *[1 mark]*.
  c) E.g. sound waves / ultrasound waves / shock waves *[1 mark]*
2 a) 2 hertz (Hz) (or s⁻¹) *[2 marks available — 1 mark for the correct value and 1 mark for the correct unit.]*
  b) i) $v = f \times \lambda$ *[1 mark — accept any rearranged version.]*
   ii) $v = f \times \lambda$ so $\lambda = \dfrac{v}{f} = \dfrac{0.5}{2} = $ **0.25 m**
[2 marks for the correct answer — otherwise 1 mark for correctly rearranging the equation and substituting the correct values into the equation.]

Remember, the wavelength of a wave is the distance from crest to crest.

   iii) $f = \dfrac{1}{T}$, so $T = \dfrac{1}{f} = \dfrac{1}{2} = $ **0.5 s**
[2 marks for the correct answer — otherwise 1 mark for correctly rearranging the equation and substituting the correct values into the equation. Allow full marks if the incorrect value from part i) is used correctly to calculate the period.]

3 a)   The amplitude is the height of the wave from its rest position to a crest *[1 mark]*.
  b)   A and C are the same. *[1 mark]*
  c) i) The wavelength — he has drawn a wavelength of 4 cm, not 2 cm *[1 mark]*.
     ii) E.g.

height of the wave from
 the rest position in cm

distance along
the wave in cm

[2 marks available for drawing a correct wave — otherwise 1 mark for drawing a wave with the correct amplitude or the correct wavelength]

Page 40: Wave Behaviour and EM Waves

1 a)   reflection *[1 mark]*
  b)   infrared *[1 mark]*
  c)   No. All electromagnetic waves travel at the same speed in free space *[1 mark]*.
2 a)   Waves bending and spreading out as they travel past edges or through gaps *[1 mark]*.
  b) i) Visible light has a very short wavelength compared to the size of a doorway *[1 mark]*, so its diffraction is too small to notice *[1 mark]*.

Light does diffract a very small amount, but it's too small for us to notice.

     ii) Disagree. Radio waves have a much longer wavelength than visible light *[1 mark]*, so they will diffract a lot more through doorways *[1 mark]*.

Pages 41-43: Uses of Electromagnetic Waves

1 a) i) the sterilisation of medical equipment. *[1 mark]*
     ii) microwaves. *[1 mark]*
     iii) reflect off the ionosphere. *[1 mark]*
  b)   data *[1 mark]*, reflect *[1 mark]*.
2 a)   The person's face *[1 mark]* because it is giving out the highest intensity of infrared radiation according to the scale *[1 mark]*, and infrared radiation is heat, so it is giving out the most heat *[1 mark]*.
  b)   E.g. night vision / to see criminals/people in the dark.
       [1 mark available for a correct use of infrared imaging.]
  c)   E.g. electrical heaters *[1 mark]* radiate infrared radiation to keep rooms or buildings warm *[1 mark]*.
3 a)   Long-wave radio signals can bend (diffract) round the mountain and reach the house *[1 mark]* because they have a long wavelength *[1 mark]*.
  b)   The TV signals reflect off the ionosphere *[1 mark]*.
  c) i) microwave radiation *[1 mark]*.
     ii) They are transmitted through the atmosphere into space, where they are picked up by a satellite receiver orbiting Earth *[1 mark]*. The satellite transmits the signal back to Earth in a different direction, where it is received by a satellite dish connected to the house *[1 mark]*.
4 a)   gamma radiation *[1 mark]*.
  b)   Treating the fruit with radiation kills the microbes in it *[1 mark]*, which means that it will stay fresh for longer *[1 mark]*.

5 a)   Disagree. Almost all of the ultraviolet radiation is absorbed *[1 mark]* by a (phosphor) coating on the inside of the glass that emits visible light instead *[1 mark]*.
  b)   A camera focuses light onto a light-sensitive film or electronic sensor *[1 mark]*. The camera can control how much light enters it by controlling how big the aperture is *[1 mark]*. The photographer can control how long the film or sensor is exposed to the light by changing the shutter speed *[1 mark]*.
6 a)   absorbed *[1 mark]*, contents *[1 mark]*.
  b)   Exposure to X-rays can cause mutations which could lead to cancer *[1 mark]*, so the driver and passengers should step outside the truck while it is exposed to X-rays to minimise their exposure *[1 mark]*.

Page 44: Dangers of Electromagnetic Waves

1 a)   Microwaves can cause internal heating of human body tissue *[1 mark]*.
  b)   E.g. infrared also has a heating effect *[1 mark]* but it has a higher frequency than microwaves and carries more energy (so it will have a greater heating effect) *[1 mark]*.
2 a)   Any two from: e.g. ultraviolet radiation is ionising / ultraviolet radiation can cause cell mutation/destruction / ultraviolet radiation can cause cancer / ultraviolet radiation can damage cells / ultraviolet radiation can cause blindness.
       [2 marks available — 1 mark for each correct answer.]
  b)   E.g. use sunscreen with ultraviolet filters that block (some of the) ultraviolet radiation from reaching your skin / limit your exposure to the sun *[1 mark]*.
3 a)   Any two from: e.g. cell destruction *[1 mark]* / cancerous changes (mutations) to cells *[1 mark]* / tissue damage *[1 mark]*.
  b)   E.g. keep exposure time to a minimum *[1 mark]*.

Page 45: Reflection of Waves

1 a) i) An imaginary line that is at right angles to the surface (at the point where the light hits the surface) *[1 mark]*.
     ii) The angle of incidence is equal to the angle of reflection *[1 mark]*.
  b) i) E.g.

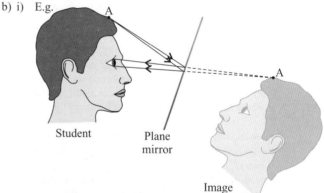

Student   Plane
                 mirror

Image

[2 marks available — 1 mark for reflected rays drawn from point A on the student to the student's eyes, and 1 mark for virtual rays drawn from the point of reflection on the mirror to point A in the image. OR 1 mark for each correctly drawn ray from point A that is reflected in the mirror and ends at the eye.]
     ii) virtual *[1 mark]*

Page 46: Refraction of Waves

1 a) E.g.

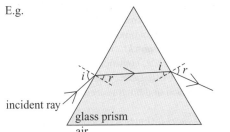

incident ray
glass prism
air

[3 marks available — 1 mark for refracting the ray towards the normal upon entering the prism, 1 mark for refracting the ray away from the normal as it leaves the prism and 1 mark for correctly labelling all the angles of incidence and refraction.]

b) E.g. Place the prism on a piece of paper and shine a ray of light at the prism. Trace the incident and emergent rays and the boundaries of the prism on the piece of paper *[1 mark]*. Remove the prism and draw in the refracted ray through the prism by joining the ends of the other two rays with a straight line *[1 mark]*. Draw in the normals using a protractor *[1 mark]* and use the protractor to measure i and r *[1 mark]*.

c) i) White light is made up of different colours of light *[1 mark]*, which have different wavelengths and so refract by different amounts at each boundary of the prism *[1 mark]*.

ii) The sides of a rectangular block are parallel *[1 mark]*, and so the rays of different colours of light bend by the same amount when they enter and leave the block and emerge parallel *[1 mark]*.

Pages 47-48: Refractive Index and Snell's Law

1 a) E.g.

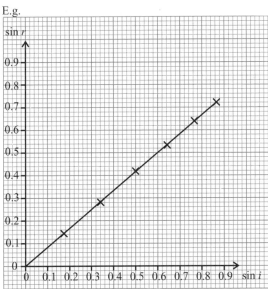

[5 marks available — 1 mark for a suitable scale chosen (more than half of the graph paper is used), 1 mark for a suitable line of best fit passing through (0, 0), 1 mark for the axes labelled with quantities and scales, 1 mark for plotting at least 5 points correctly to the nearest half square, 1 further mark for plotting all 6 points correctly to the nearest square.]

b) Gradient $= \dfrac{\sin r}{\sin i} = \dfrac{0.5}{0.6} = 0.833...$

$n = \dfrac{\sin i}{\sin r}$ so $0.833... = \dfrac{1}{n}$ and $n = \dfrac{1}{0.833...} = 1.20$ (to 3 s.f.)

So refractive index = **1.20 (to 3 s.f.)**

[4 marks for correct answer, otherwise 1 mark for calculating the gradient, 1 mark for relating the gradient to the equation linking n, i and r, and 1 mark for correct substitution of gradient into rearranged equation to find n. Deduct 1 mark for giving units.]

2 a) $i = 45°$

$n = \dfrac{\sin i}{\sin r}$ so $\sin r = \dfrac{\sin i}{n} = \dfrac{\sin 45°}{1.514} = 0.467...$

So $r = \sin^{-1}(0.467...) =$ **27.84° (to 4 s.f.)**

[4 marks for correct answer, otherwise 1 mark for using correct equation, 1 mark for correct substitution and 1 mark for correct rearrangement.]

b) The separation happens when different colours refract by different amounts *[1 mark]*, but light doesn't refract when it crosses a boundary along the normal *[1 mark]*.

c) Angle of incidence for violet light $= i = 45°$

$\sin r = \dfrac{\sin i}{n} = \dfrac{\sin 45°}{1.528} = 0.4627...$

$\Rightarrow r = \sin^{-1}(0.4627...) = 27.57°$ (to 4 s.f.)

Then subtract this angle from the angle of refraction of red light to get:

$\theta = 27.84 - 27.57 =$ **0.27°**

[4 marks for correct answer, otherwise 1 mark for correct rearrangement of the equation to find r, 1 mark for correct angle of refraction of violet light and 1 mark for correctly subtracting one angle from the other. Allow the marks if the answer given to part a) is used correctly. Do not deduct marks for using an incorrect number of significant figures in calculations.]

Page 49: Refractive Index and Critical Angles

1 a) When light is incident at a boundary between materials at an angle greater than the critical angle, causing the light to be reflected back at the boundary (total internal reflection) *[1 mark]*.

b) Bending an optical fibre sharply will result in a lot of light meeting the boundary at an angle that is smaller than or equal to than the critical angle *[1 mark]*. This means a lot of light will escape the optical fibre, so less light will be used to make the image *[1 mark]*.

2 a) The angle of incidence such that the angle of refraction is 90° (for light travelling from a denser material to a less dense material) *[1 mark]*.

b) It must be lower than 63.2° (the critical angle) as it is crossing the boundary *[1 mark]*.

c) It will be reflected back into the acrylic (total internal reflection) *[1 mark]*.

d) $n = \dfrac{1}{\sin C} = \dfrac{1}{\sin 41.8°} =$ **1.50 (to 3 s.f.)**

[3 marks for correct answer, otherwise 1 mark for using the correct equation and 1 mark for substituting correct values into the equation. Deduct 1 mark for giving units.]

Page 50: Analogue and Digital Signals

1 a) Digital *[1 mark]*. Digital signals can only take two values, and the CD only has two possible 'values' that can be detected — a pit or a bump *[1 mark]*.

b) The information on the vinyl record can take a range of different values (it's analogue), whereas the CD can only take two *[1 mark]*.

c) It's difficult to tell from a noisy analogue signal, like the record signal, what the original signal looked like *[1 mark]*. However noise on digital signals (like the CD signal) can be ignored, as it doesn't change whether the signal is a 0 or a 1 *[1 mark]*.

d)

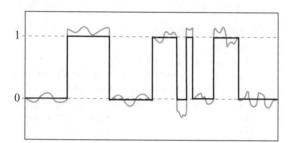

[2 marks available — 1 mark for turning the correct noisy parts horizontal, and 1 mark for a signal that is always either 0 or 1.]

e) E.g. digital signals can be multiplexed so many signals can be carried on the same wire or electromagnetic wave at the same time, whereas analogue signals can suffer interference when multiplexed / digital signals can undergo quantisation without losing much information, whereas analogue signals lose some information in this process / noise can easily be removed from digital signals whereas noise removal can lead to deterioration of the quality of analogue signals. *[1 mark for a correct answer.]*

Pages 51-52: Sound Waves

1 a) i) The distance between the two microphones is 1 wavelength *[1 mark]* so use $v = f \times \lambda$ to calculate the speed of sound.
ii) $v = f \times \lambda = 50 \times 6.8 =$ **340 metres per second (m/s)** *[4 marks for correct answer, otherwise 1 mark for using the correct equation, 1 mark for substituting correct values into the equation and 1 mark for the correct units.]*

b) i) time period *[1 mark]*
ii) One time cycle is 8 divisions long, so $T = 0.005 \times 8 = 0.04$ s
$f = \dfrac{1}{T} = \dfrac{1}{0.04} =$ **25 Hz**
[2 marks for correct answer, otherwise 1 mark for substituting correctly into correct equation.]
iii) E.g.

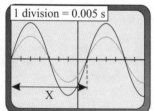

1 division = 0.005 s

X

[1 mark for increasing the amplitude of the wave. Award no marks if the frequency of the wave has changed.]

2 a) Echoes are caused by the reflection of sound waves from the surfaces of the drama hall and on the field there are no walls for the waves to reflect off *[1 mark]*.

b) It may refract (change direction) *[1 mark]*.

c) i) 20 – 20 000 Hz *[1 mark]*
ii) The pitch is lower, i.e. his voice will sound lower *[1 mark]*. This is because the frequency of the sound waves he produces is lower and pitch is determined by frequency *[1 mark]*.

d) The sound waves diffract (spread out) as they pass through the doorway of the hall *[1 mark]*.

Section 4 — Energy Resources and Energy Transfer

Page 53: Conservation of Energy

1

Device	Energy input	Useful energy output
A spring-loaded catapult	(elastic) potential energy	kinetic energy
A portable radio	chemical energy	sound energy
E.g. a heater	electrical energy	heat energy

[3 marks available — 1 mark for each correct answer]

2 a) transferred *[1 mark]*, created *[1 mark]*

b) 100 J of energy *[1 mark]* — energy is conserved, so the total output energy must equal the total input energy *[1 mark]*.
The total output energy is 20 J + 80 J = 100 J.

Page 54: Efficiency

1 a) light (energy) *[1 mark]*

b) i) efficiency $= \dfrac{\text{useful energy output}}{\text{total energy input}}$ *[1 mark]*
ii) efficiency $= \dfrac{\text{useful energy output}}{\text{total energy input}} = \dfrac{8}{20} =$ **0.4 (or 40%)**
[2 marks if answer correct, otherwise 1 mark for correct substitution of values into the formula.]

c) efficiency $= \dfrac{\text{useful energy output}}{\text{total energy input}}$
$\Rightarrow$ total energy input $= \dfrac{\text{useful energy output}}{\text{efficiency}}$
$= \dfrac{10}{0.55} =$ **18 J (to 2 s.f.)**
[2 marks if answer correct, otherwise 1 mark for correct rearrangement of the formula and correct substitution of values into the formula.]

d) Disagree — torch B has a lower energy input than torch A, i.e. it transfers less energy per second than torch A *[1 mark — allow the mark if an incorrect value from part c) has been used correctly]*.
You receive no marks for this question if you agreed with the student's claim.

Page 55: Energy Transfers

1 a) nuclear → heat *[1 mark]*

 b) E.g. electrical energy → heat energy, not useful. / electrical energy → sound energy (in the speakers), useful. / electrical energy → light energy in the screen, useful.
 [2 marks — 1 mark for a correct energy transfer, 1 mark for saying whether this is a useful transfer or not.]

2 a) gravitational potential energy *[1 mark]*

 b) E.g. Chemical energy is transferred to the kinetic energy of his arms and the bar by his muscles *[1 mark]*. Some of this kinetic energy is converted into gravitational potential energy as the bar is raised *[1 mark]*.

 c) Gravitational potential energy will be converted into kinetic energy *[1 mark]*.

Pages 56-57: Sankey Diagrams

1 a) 10 J *[1 mark]*
You know the total input energy is 200 J. The input energy arrow is 20 squares wide, so the value of each square must be 200 J ÷ 20 = 10 J.

 b) 50 J *[1 mark]*
The useful energy arrow is 5 squares wide, and each square represents 10 J. So the amount of energy that's usefully transferred = 5 × 10 J = 50 J

 c) E.g.

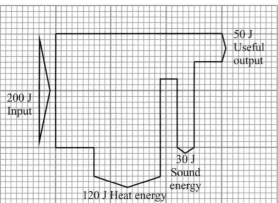

[3 marks available — 1 mark for three arrow widths drawn correctly, 1 mark for all four arrow widths drawn correctly, 1 mark for all arrows being correctly labelled.]

2 a) E.g. heat energy/sound energy *[1 mark]*

 b) Gravitational potential energy of lifted weight = 100 − 50 − 20 = 30 kJ *[1 mark]*

 c) E.g.

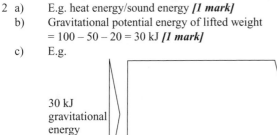

[3 marks available — 1 mark for drawing a recognisable Sankey diagram, 1 mark for all of the arrows being drawn in roughly the correct proportions, 1 mark for all of the arrows being correctly labelled.]

Page 58: Heat Transfer

1 a) Conduction *[1 mark]* and radiation *[1 mark]*

 b) Flask C *[1 mark]*.
There is a larger temperature difference between flask C and the surrounding gel *[1 mark]*.
You receive no marks for this question if you answered A or B.

2 a) Conduction *[1 mark]*. As particles in the solid are heated they gain kinetic energy *[1 mark]*. The particles collide with their neighbouring particles and transfer some of their extra kinetic energy to them, transferring the heat through the solid *[1 mark]*

 b) Radiation is where energy is transferred/emitted in the form of electromagnetic waves/infrared radiation *[1 mark]*.

Page 59: Heat Convection

1 a) solid *[1 mark]* because the particles are not free to move *[1 mark]*.

 b) i) E.g.

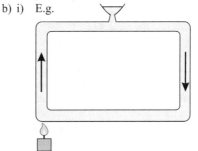

[1 mark for 2 arrows drawn anywhere inside the glass tube showing the correct flow of water]

 ii) The water particles near the heat source gain energy *[1 mark]*. This causes the water near the heat source to expand and become less dense and rise up the pipe *[1 mark]*. Colder, denser water elsewhere in the pipe is displaced and moves to replace this heated water *[1 mark]*.

 c) The transfer of heat through a copper pan *[1 mark]*.

Page 60: Reducing Energy Transfers

1 a) The hairs 'stand up' to trap a layer of insulating air around the body *[1 mark]* to limit the amount of heat lost by convection *[1 mark]*.

 b) E.g. wearing (more) clothes *[1 mark]* — layering clothes will trap layers of air, which will help to reduce heat loss by conduction *[1 mark]*.
[1 mark for a correct suggestion, 1 mark for an explanation naming the method of heat transfer it reduces.]

2 a) i) conduction *[1 mark]*.

 ii) E.g. it will help stop a convection current being set up in the air gap (and so reduce heat loss by convection). / It will reduce radiation across the gap (as it will absorb or reflect most of the heat radiated from the inside wall). / The foam and air trapped in it are both insulators, and so will help reduce heat loss by conduction from the home.
[1 mark for naming a type of heat transfer and correctly explaining how energy transfer is reduced].

 b) E.g. any two from: Installing double glazing *[1 mark]* — the air gap between the layers of glass will help reduce the amount of energy being transferred through the window by conduction *[1 mark]*. / Fitting draught-proofing strips around the windows *[1 mark]* will help to reduce the amount of heat escaping as draughts *[1 mark]*. / Putting up curtains/buying thicker curtains *[1 mark]* — curtains will help to reduce the amount of warm air in a room reaching the window, and so reduce heat loss by conduction/radiation *[1 mark]*.

Pages 61-62: Work and Power

1   rate *[1 mark]*, energy *[1 mark]*, watts *[1 mark]*

2 a) i) The energy transferred when a force moves an object *[1 mark]*.

    ii) 50 joules (J) *[1 mark]*

  b) i) Work done = force × distance moved in the direction of the force / $W = F \times d$ *[1 mark]*

    ii) $W = F \times d \Rightarrow d = \dfrac{W}{F} = \dfrac{50}{250} = $ **0.2 m**

      [2 marks if answer correct, otherwise 1 mark for correct rearrangement of the formula and correct substitution of values into the formula.]

3 a) $P = \dfrac{W}{t} \Rightarrow W = P \times t = 150 \times (10 \times 60) = 90\,000$ J = **90 kJ**

    [2 marks if answer correct, otherwise 1 mark for correct rearrangement of the formula and correct substitution of values into the formula.]

  b) $W = F \times d = 155 \times 1.2 = $ **186 J**

    [2 marks if answer correct, otherwise 1 mark for correct substitution of values into the formula.]

  c) E.g. The maximum speed will increase. The motor has a higher power rating and so will transfer more chemical energy (from fuel) into kinetic energy (of the boat) each second.
The boat will have to be refuelled more often because more energy is transferred per second. So more input energy from the fuel is needed, and so more fuel will be used per second.
[4 marks available — 1 mark for saying the maximum speed would increase, 1 mark for supporting explanation. 1 mark for saying the boat would need to be refuelled more often, 1 mark for a supporting explanation]

4   Disagree — the tyres were identical and so the students will have used the same force. $W = F \times d$, so student 1 must have done the most work as they dragged the tyre furthest. $P = W \div t$, student 1 did three times the work student 2 did, but it took him six times longer. This means student 2 was actually more powerful than student 1.
[3 marks available — 1 mark for disagreeing and stating that student 1 did more work, 1 mark for saying $P = W \div t$ and 1 mark for showing student 2 was more powerful.]

Pages 63-64: Kinetic and Gravitational Potential Energy

1 a) movement. *[1 mark]*

  b) work is done to convert kinetic energy into gravitational potential energy. *[1 mark]*

  c) gravitational potential energy and kinetic energy. *[1 mark]*

2 a) 4.0 J *[1 mark]*

  b) kinetic energy = $\dfrac{1}{2}$ × mass × speed² (KE = $\dfrac{1}{2} \times m \times v^2$) *[1 mark]*

  c) $KE = \dfrac{1}{2}mv^2$
$\Rightarrow v = \sqrt{\dfrac{2 \times KE}{m}} = \sqrt{\dfrac{2 \times 4.0}{0.1}} = $ **8.9 m/s (to 2 s.f.)**
[3 marks if answer correct, otherwise 1 mark for correct rearrangement of the formula and 1 mark for correct substitution of values into the formula.]

3 a) $KE = \dfrac{1}{2}mv^2 = \dfrac{1}{2} \times 105 \times 2.39^2 = $ **300 J (to 3 s.f.)**
[3 marks if answer correct, otherwise 1 mark for using the correct formula and 1 mark for correct substitution of values into the formula.]

  b) i) gravitational potential energy = mass × g × height (GPE = $m \times g \times h$) *[1 mark]*

    ii) $GPE = m \times g \times h = 105 \times 10 \times 20.2 = $ **21 200 J (to 3 s.f.)**
[2 marks if answer correct, otherwise 1 mark for correct substitution of values into the formula.]

    iii) It's converted to kinetic energy *[1 mark]*.

  c) Total kinetic energy = initial KE + loss in GPE
          = 300 + 21 200 = 21 500 J

    $KE = \dfrac{1}{2}mv^2$
    $\Rightarrow v = \sqrt{\dfrac{2 \times KE}{m}} = \sqrt{\dfrac{2 \times 21\,500}{105}} = $ **20.2 m/s (to 3 s.f.)**
[4 marks if answer correct, otherwise 1 mark for correctly identifying the total kinetic energy, 1 mark for correct rearrangement of the formula and 1 mark for correct substitution of values into the formula.]

Page 65: Non-Renewable Energy and Power Stations

1 a) wind *[1 mark]*

  b) The heat energy is used to turn the water into steam *[1 mark]*. The steam is used to drive turbines — transferring heat energy into kinetic energy *[1 mark]*. The turbine drives a generator — the kinetic energy of the generator is transferred into electrical energy *[1 mark]*.

  c) E.g. any two from:
Burning natural gas releases a lot of energy for a relatively low cost *[1 mark]* / energy from natural gas doesn't rely on the weather or time of day (it's reliable) *[1 mark]* / no new technology or spending is needed to set up natural gas power stations — we have a lot already *[1 mark]*.

  d) i) Disagree — sulfur dioxide is only released by burning coal and oil *[1 mark]*.

    ii) E.g. natural gas supplies will eventually run out (they're non-renewable) *[1 mark]*.

Page 66: Nuclear, Wind and Geothermal Energy

1 a) Nuclear energy is transferred into heat energy in nuclear reactions *[1 mark]*.

  b) i) Nuclear fuels aren't burned and so don't release any greenhouse gases (e.g. carbon dioxide) *[1 mark]* that contribute to global warming *[1 mark]*.

    ii) E.g. any two from:
Processing or transporting the nuclear fuel before it is used causes atmospheric pollution *[1 mark]* / nuclear power stations carry the risk of major catastrophes (like Chernobyl), which have a huge impact on the environment *[1 mark]* / radioactive waste is difficult to dispose of and is harmful to the environment *[1 mark]*.

2 a) i) kinetic *[1 mark]*, kinetic *[1 mark]*, electrical *[1 mark]*.

    ii) Advantage — e.g.:
Wind farms have low running costs (as there are no fuel costs) *[1 mark]* / wind is a renewable resource (it won't run out) *[1 mark]* / wind farms cause no atmospheric pollution *[1 mark]*.
Disadvantage — e.g.:
Some people think wind farms spoil the view/make too much noise *[1 mark]* / a lot of wind farms are needed to generate the same amount of electricity as a fossil fuel power station *[1 mark]* / wind speed varies, so they're not particularly reliable *[1 mark]* / wind farms usually require specific (remote) locations, so building and maintenance work is expensive *[1 mark]* / you can't increase the supply of electricity when demand is high *[1 mark]*.

  b) Advantage — e.g.:
Geothermal energy is a renewable resource *[1 mark]* / no fuel is required so there are low running costs *[1 mark]* / geothermal power stations have very little impact on the environment once set up *[1 mark]*.
Disadvantage — e.g.:
There are high initial costs in drilling down several km *[1 mark]* / the cost of building a power station is often high compared to the amount of energy obtained *[1 mark]* / the possible locations for power stations are very limited *[1 mark]*.

Page 67: Solar and Wave Energy

1 a) Kinetic energy *[1 mark]*.
  b) Disagree — the size of waves is variable and uncontrollable, and so this can be an unreliable method of generating electricity *[1 mark]*. The running costs are low, but wave power stations are initially expensive to set up *[1 mark]*.
2 a) A solar cell *[1 mark]*
  b) E.g. solar hot water panels — they absorb energy from the Sun to heat water inside them. This hot water can then be supplied to the home *[1 mark]*.
  c) E.g. the cost of connecting solar cells to the National Grid is high compared to the amount of electricity they generate *[1 mark]*. It is often not practical to connect them to the National Grid. *[1 mark]*.

Page 68: Generating Electricity Using Water

1 a) The water's gravitational potential energy is converted to kinetic energy of the turbines *[1 mark]*, which is converted to electrical energy by a generator *[1 mark]*.
  b) E.g. any two from: they can cause the loss or destruction of habitats *[1 mark]* / rotting vegetation in dams releases methane *[1 mark]*.
  c) Pumped storage *[1 mark]*.
  d) E.g. any two from:
     They cause no atmospheric pollution *[1 mark]* / they use a renewable energy source *[1 mark]* / there are no fuel costs *[1 mark]* / maintenance and running costs are low *[1 mark]* / tides are regular and predictable, so this is a fairly reliable energy source *[1 mark]*.

Section 5 — Solids, Liquids and Gases

Pages 69-70: Pressure and Density

1 a) The densities of each of the toy soldiers are the same, but their masses may vary *[1 mark]*.
  b) i) The volume of the toy soldier *[1 mark]*.
       The mass of the toy soldier *[1 mark]*.
     ii) E.g. measure the mass of the toy soldier using the mass balance *[1 mark]*. Measure the volume of the soldier by first filling the measuring cylinder with enough water to submerge the toy soldier and taking a reading of the volume *[1 mark]*. Then submerge the toy soldier in the water and take another reading of the volume *[1 mark]*. Calculate the volume of the toy solder by subtracting the initial volume reading from the final volume reading *[1 mark]*. Divide the mass of the toy solider by the volume of the toy soldier to find the density *[1 mark]*.

With questions where you have to describe a method, make sure your description is clear and detailed. You could also pick up some of the marks by describing how you'd do repeats, take averages and other ways in which you'd make it a fair test.

2 a) equal *[1 mark]*, greater *[1 mark]*
  b) i) pressure = $\frac{\text{force}}{\text{area}}$ ($p = \frac{F}{A}$) *[1 mark]*
     ii) pressure = $\frac{\text{force}}{\text{area}} = \frac{18}{0.45}$ = **40 Pa**
        [2 marks if answer correct, otherwise 1 mark for correct substitution of values into the equation.]

3 a) pressure difference = height × density × g ($p = h \times \rho \times g$) *[1 mark]*
  b) i) density = $\frac{\text{mass}}{\text{volume}} = \frac{500}{0.5}$
        = **1000 kilograms per metre cubed (kg/m³)**
        [4 marks if answer correct, otherwise 1 mark for using correct equation, 1 mark for correct substitution and 1 mark for the correct unit.]

     ii) $p = h \times \rho \times g \Rightarrow h = \frac{p}{\rho \times g} = \frac{240\,000}{1000 \times 10}$ = **24 m**
        [3 marks if answer correct, otherwise 1 mark for correct rearrangement of the equation and 1 mark for correct substitution of values into the equation. Allow marks if incorrect value of density is used from part b) i)]

Page 71: Changes of State

1 a) i) Particles are held close together in a fixed, regular pattern *[1 mark]*. They vibrate about fixed positions *[1 mark]*.
     ii) gas(es) *[1 mark]*
  b) i) melting *[1 mark]*
     ii) When the solid substance is heated the particles inside it gain energy and vibrate faster *[1 mark]*. When the temperature gets high enough, they start moving fast enough to overcome the forces of attraction between them and start moving around (i.e. the substance becomes a liquid) *[1 mark]*.
  c) i) Evaporation *[1 mark]*. A liquid can evaporate at any temperature whereas boiling happens only at the boiling point *[1 mark]*. Particles in the liquid can only evaporate if they are travelling in the right direction, fast enough to overcome the attractive forces of the other particles in the liquid, whereas when a liquid boils, all of the particles have enough energy to escape *[1 mark]*.
     ii) When a liquid evaporates the fastest particles are most likely to escape the liquid *[1 mark]*. When they do, the average speed/kinetic energy of the remaining particles in the liquid decreases *[1 mark]*. The drop in average speed/kinetic energy causes a drop in temperature *[1 mark]*.

Page 72: Particle Theory and Temperature in Gases

1 a) i) The average speed decreases *[1 mark]*
     ii) The energy of the particles in a substance decreases with temperature *[1 mark]*. There is a minimum energy that the particles can have, so there is a minimum temperature *[1 mark]*.
     iii) –273 °C *[1 mark]*
  b)

Temperature (K)	Temperature (°C)
10	–263
904	631

[2 marks available — 1 mark for each correct temperature.]
To convert from the Kelvin scale to the Celsius scale just subtract 273, and to convert from the Celsius scale to the Kelvin scale add 273.

2 a) i) Brownian motion *[1 mark]*.
     ii) The motion suggests that the smoke particles are being moved by collisions with lighter gas particles *[1 mark]* which travel at high speeds *[1 mark]* (as described by particle theory).
  b) The average kinetic energy will increase by a factor of 3, (it will triple) *[1 mark]*.

Page 73: Particle Theory and Pressure in Gases

1 a) i) The pressure increases *[1 mark]*. This is because the volume decrease leads to the number of collisions between particles and the walls of the balloon increasing *[1 mark]* and so the force applied by the particles to the balloon walls increases *[1 mark]*.

ii) $p_1 V_1 = p_2 V_2 \Rightarrow p_2 = \dfrac{p_1 V_1}{V_2} = \dfrac{98 \times 0.014}{0.013} = 105.5$ kPa
$= \mathbf{110}$ **kPa (to 2 s.f.)**

[3 marks if answer correct, otherwise 1 mark for correct rearrangement of the equation and 1 mark for correct substitution of values into the equation.]

b) As the gas is heated, the average kinetic energy of the particles increases *[1 mark]*. This means they collide with the walls more often *[1 mark]*, increasing the outwards force/ pressure on the walls of the balloon *[1 mark]*.

2 $\dfrac{p_1}{T_1} = \dfrac{p_2}{T_2} \Rightarrow p_2 = \dfrac{p_1 \times T_2}{T_1} = \dfrac{107 \times 405}{288} = \mathbf{150}$ **kPa (to 3 s.f.)**
[3 marks if answer correct, otherwise 1 mark for correct rearrangement of the equation and 1 mark for correct substitution of values into the equation.]

Section 6 — Magnetism and Electromagnetism

Page 74: Magnets and Magnetic Fields

1 a) E.g. Put the magnets on a piece of paper and place many compasses in different places between the magnets to show the magnetic field at those points *[1 mark]*. The compasses will line up with the magnetic field lines *[1 mark]*.
You could also use iron filings to shown the pattern.

b) E.g.

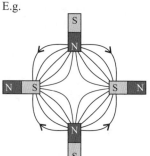

[2 marks for four correct arrows, otherwise 1 mark for two correct arrows, each one placed between a different pair of magnets. Do not award any marks for contradicting arrows.]

c) i) The field is uniform *[1 mark]*
ii) Attraction *[1 mark]* — opposite poles are facing each other so there will be a force of attraction between them *[1 mark]*.

2 a) A material that is attracted by a magnet. / A material that becomes magnetised when placed in a magnetic field *[1 mark]*.

b) The north pole of the bar magnet induces a south/opposite pole in the head of the nail *[1 mark]* and the opposite poles attract each other *[1 mark]*.

Pages 75-76: Electromagnetism

1 a) a magnetic field is created around the copper rod *[1 mark]*.
b)

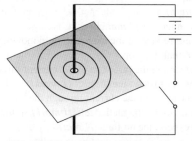

[1 mark for drawing concentric circles centred around the hole in the card.]

c)

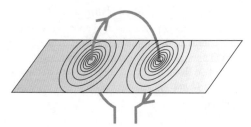

[1 mark]

2 a) A solenoid, or coil of wire (with an iron core) *[1 mark]*.
b)

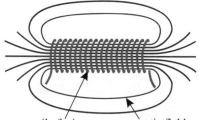

coil of wire   magnetic field

Inside the coil, the field is strong and uniform. Outside the coil, the field is the same as that of a bar magnet.
[2 marks — 1 mark for showing by sketch or for saying that the field is uniform and strong inside the coil and 1 mark for showing by sketch or saying that the field is like that of a bar magnet outside the coil.]

c) When the electromagnet is turned on, current flows through the coil of wire and produces a magnetic field *[1 mark]*. Iron is a magnetic material, so magnetism is induced in it and the bar is attracted to it *[1 mark]*. When the current stops, there is no longer a magnetic field around the electromagnet *[1 mark]* so the bar is no longer attracted to the electromagnet and drops *[1 mark]*.

d) i) A magnetic material that loses its induced magnetism quickly *[1 mark]*.
ii) Magnetically hard materials don't lose their magnetism quickly *[1 mark]*, so when the electromagnet is turned off the core will stay magnetic for a while and still attract the iron bar, meaning the crane won't drop the iron bar *[1 mark]*.

Page 77: The Motor Effect

1 a) i) A current-carrying wire in a magnetic field experiences a
force *[1 mark]*.
   ii) upwards *[1 mark]*
  b) i) The force will increase *[1 mark]*.
   ii) Reversing the direction of the magnetic field/moving
the magnet so that the loop wraps around the other pole
[1 mark]. Reversing the direction of the current/direction
that the wire wraps round the magnet *[1 mark]*.
  c) The electrons that form the current through the bar are
moving parallel to the magnetic field *[1 mark]* so they (and
the bar) will experience no force *[1 mark]*.

Page 78: Electric Motors and Loudspeakers

1 a) E.g.

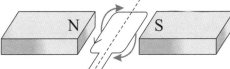

*[1 mark for any indication that the current goes
anticlockwise.]*
  b) After 90° the force on the top arm will act upwards and the
force on the bottom arm will act downwards, so the forces
will oppose the rotation of the loop *[1 mark]*.
  c) By swapping the direction of the current/contacts every half
turn (using a split-ring commutator) *[1 mark]* so the forces
on the loop always act in a way that keeps the loop rotating
[1 mark].
  d) Any of: Increase the current *[1 mark]*. / Increase the number
of turns on the loop *[1 mark]*. / Increase the strength of the
magnetic field *[1 mark]*.
2 When the a.c. current flows through the coil of wire in the
magnetic field of the permanent magnet, the coil of wire
experiences a force *[1 mark]*. The force causes the coil, and
so the cone, to move *[1 mark]*. The a.c. current is constantly
changing direction so the force on the coil is constantly
changing so the cone vibrates back and forth *[1 mark]*. The
vibrations cause the air to vibrate and cause sound waves
[1 mark].

Pages 79-80: Electromagnetic Induction

1 a) As the wheel rotates, the magnet rotates inside the coil of
wire *[1 mark]*. This creates a changing magnetic field in the
coil of wire which induces a voltage *[1 mark]*.
  b) Any two of: Increase the strength of the magnet *[1 mark]*. /
Increase the number of turns on the coil of wire *[1 mark]*. /
Increase the speed of rotation of the magnet *[1 mark]*.
  c) Agree. There will be a changing magnetic field through the
wire when the magnet rotates in either direction *[1 mark]*.
2 a) Rotating the handle causes the coil to rotate (move) within
the magnetic field, so a voltage (and so current) is induced in
the circuit *[1 mark]*. The direction of the wire's movement
in relation to the magnetic field changes every half turn
and so the direction of the current/voltage induced changes
[1 mark].

  b) E.g.

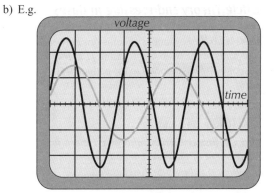

*[2 marks available — 1 mark for drawing a trace with
a larger voltage than the original trace and 1 mark for
drawing a trace with a higher frequency than the original
trace.]*
  c) The trace would be the same as when the coil is rotating and
the magnets are fixed *[1 mark]*.

Pages 81-82: Transformers

1 a) Step-down, because the voltage decreases (from 240 V to
12 V) *[1 mark]*.
  b) i) Power = current × voltage or $P = I \times V$ *[1 mark]*
   ii) $P = I \times V = 0.25 \times 240 = \mathbf{60\,W}$
*[2 marks for correct answer, otherwise 1 mark for
substituting correct values into the equation.]*
   iii) If the transformer is 100 % efficient, input power = output
power, so output power = 60 W.
$P = I \times V$ so $I = \dfrac{P}{V} = \dfrac{60}{12} = \mathbf{5\,A}$
*[3 marks for correct answer, otherwise 1 mark for the
correct output power and 1 mark for substituting correctly
into rearranged equation.]*
  c) Disagree. No current should flow through the core of a
transformer *[1 mark]*.
2 a) A step-up transformer is used to increase the voltage of
electricity supplied by the power stations to be very high
[1 mark]. A higher voltage means less current for a given
power ($V = I \times R$) and so less energy lost as heat *[1 mark]*.
Step-down transformers are then used to bring the voltage
of the supply back down to a safe level to be supplied to the
consumer *[1 mark]*.
  b) i) $\dfrac{\text{input (primary) voltage}}{\text{output (secondary) voltage}} = \dfrac{\text{number of turns on primary}}{\text{number of turns on secondary}}$
or $\dfrac{V_p}{V_s} = \dfrac{n_p}{n_s}$ *[1 mark]*
   ii) $\dfrac{V_p}{V_s} = \dfrac{n_p}{n_s}$ so $V_s = \dfrac{n_s}{n_p} \times V_p = 16 \times 25\,000 = \mathbf{400\,000\,V}$
*[4 marks available, otherwise 1 mark for saying
$\dfrac{n_s}{n_p} = 16$, 1 mark for rearranging the equation correctly
and 1 mark for substituting correctly into the equation.]*
  c) If the current was direct, it wouldn't change so the magnetic
field created by the primary coil wouldn't change *[1 mark]*.
This means the magnetic field through the secondary coil
wouldn't change *[1 mark]*, so no voltage would be induced
across it *[1 mark]*.

Section 7 — Radioactivity and Particles

Page 83: Radioactivity

1 a) i)

Particle	Charge	Number present in an atom of iodine-131
Proton	positive	53
Neutron	zero	78
Electron	negative	53

[3 marks — 1 mark for each correct answer]

   ii)   protons and neutrons *[1 mark]*

  b)   Atoms with the same atomic number but a different mass number *[1 mark]*.

Isotopes have the same number of protons but a different number of neutrons, so they have the same atomic number (no. of protons) but a different mass number (no. of protons and neutrons). The number of protons always equals the number of electrons in a neutral atom (i.e. not an ion).

  c) i)   background radiation *[1 mark]*

      ii) Any two from: e.g. air / food / building materials / soils / rocks / radiation from space (cosmic rays) / living things *[2 marks — 1 mark for each correct answer]*.

  d)   gamma (rays) *[1 mark]*, alpha (particles) *[1 mark]*, beta (particles) *[1 mark]*

Page 84: The Three Kinds of Radioactivity

1 a) i)   ion *[1 mark]*

      ii) Alpha (particles) *[1 mark]* because they are large and heavy, so they collide with lots of atoms, causing ionisation *[1 mark]*.

  b) i)   gamma (rays) *[1 mark]*

      ii) beta (particles) *[1 mark]*

2 a)   Beta (particles) *[1 mark]*, because it passes through the paper, but not the aluminium, so it is moderately penetrating in comparison to the other two *[1 mark]*.

  b)   Geiger-Muller detector / photographic film *[1 mark]*

Pages 85-86: Alpha Scattering and Nuclear Equations

1 a)   Gold (Au). A more positively charged nucleus (with a higher atomic number) will deflect the particles more *[1 mark]*.

  b)   They will be deflected less *[1 mark]*.

  c)   They will be deflected less *[1 mark]*.

2 a)   An atom contains a small, positively charged nucleus *[1 mark]* where most of the mass of the atom is contained *[1 mark]*. The rest of the atom is mostly empty space *[1 mark]*.

  b)   They fired a beam of alpha particles *[1 mark]* at thin gold foil and measured how much the alpha particles were deflected by *[1 mark]*.

  c)   The fact that most of the alpha particles went straight through the foil, but some bounced back towards them supports the idea of a positively charged nucleus which repels the positive alpha particles *[1 mark]*. The fact that only a few bounced straight back supports the idea that the mass is concentrated in a small centre *[1 mark]*. The fact that most particles went straight through supports the idea that most of the atom is just empty space *[1 mark]*.

3 a) i) $_{-1}^{0}e$

        [2 marks — 1 mark for each correct number.]

      ii) The atomic number increases by 1 *[1 mark]* and the mass number stays the same *[1 mark]*.

  b) i)   The atomic number doesn't change *[1 mark]* and neither does the mass number *[1 mark]*.

      ii) $_{84}^{199}Po \rightarrow\ _{82}^{195}Pb +\ _{2}^{4}\alpha +\ _{0}^{0}\gamma$

        [4 marks — 1 mark each for the α and the γ correct and 1 mark each for the mass and atomic numbers of Po.]

Pages 87-88: Half-Life

1 a)   To get a measure of the background radiation *[1 mark]* so that the processed results can take it into account *[1 mark]*.

  b)

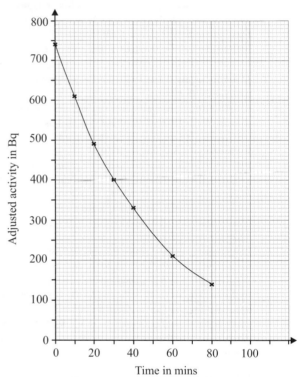

[1 mark for a graph of suitable size (at least half the graph paper used), 1 mark for a curve of best fit, 1 mark for axes labelled (with variables and units), 2 marks for correctly plotted points. Deduct up to 2 marks for incorrectly plotted points, 1 mark per incorrect point.]

  c)   34 minutes ± 2 min *[2 marks for correct answer, otherwise 1 mark for evidence of using the graph correctly to find the half-life].*

  d)   The older sample would have a lower count rate/activity (Bq) to begin with *[1 mark]* because more of its nuclei will have already decayed so it will emit less radiation *[1 mark]*.

The samples are identical so they'll have the same half-life.

2   decreases *[1 mark]*, half *[1 mark]*, nuclei *[1 mark]*.

3 a) i) 2 × 60 = 120 seconds
        120 ÷ 40 = 3 half-lives
        8000 ÷ 2 = 4000, 4000 ÷ 2 = 2000, 2000 ÷ 2 = **1000 Bq**
        [2 marks for the correct answer, otherwise 1 mark for calculating the number of half-lives.]

      ii) 8000 ÷ 2 = 4000, 4000 ÷ 2 = 2000, 2000 ÷ 2 = 1000, 1000 ÷ 2 = 500, 500 ÷ 2 = 250, 250 ÷ 2 = 125. So it takes 6 half-lives to drop to less than 200 Bq.
        6 × 40 = 240 seconds
        240 ÷ 60 = **4 mins**
        [3 marks for the correct answer, otherwise 1 mark for calculating the number of half-lives and 1 mark for calculating the number of seconds.]

  b)   Paul. Sample size doesn't affect half-life but different isotopes do have different half-lives *[1 mark]*.

Pages 89-90: Uses of Nuclear Radiation

1 a) i)

Alpha	
Beta	
Gamma	✗

[1 mark]

ii) Alpha and beta wouldn't be detected on the surface above the pipe *[1 mark]* because they would be blocked by the pipe and the surrounding ground *[1 mark]*. / Only gamma would be able to pass through the pipe and ground *[1 mark]* and so be detectable at the surface above the pipe *[1 mark]*.

b) E.g. The source of radiation could be injected into the pipeline before the first point where it is thought to be leaking *[1 mark]*. The radiation sensor would then be passed along the surface above the pipe *[1 mark]*. Where there is a leak, radiation will escape from the pipe and there will be a high reading above that part of the pipe *[1 mark]*.

c) Disagree. The company uses a source with a short half-life *[1 mark]*. The activity of the source will rapidly decrease to a safe level *[1 mark]*.

2 a) The iodine-123 is absorbed in the same way that the patient's body normally absorbs iodine, but gives out radiation which can be detected outside the body *[1 mark]*. The patient is given iodine-123 and the amount of radiation emitted from the thyroid gland is monitored to check whether it is absorbing iodine properly *[1 mark]*.

b) Alpha particles can't penetrate tissue/would be blocked by the body *[1 mark]*, so you couldn't detect them outside of the body *[1 mark]*. Alpha particles are also strongly ionising *[1 mark]* so they're dangerous to use as medical tracers *[1 mark]*.

c) Technetium-99m because it's got a short half-life *[1 mark]*, which means it's easier to detect because its activity is higher/ won't be very radioactive inside the patient for long *[1 mark]*.

3 One half-life: 1:20 000 000. Two half-lives: 1:40 000 000. Three half-lives: 1:80 000 000.
3 × 5730 = **17 190 years.**
[3 marks, otherwise 1 mark for correctly stating 3 half-lives and 1 mark for attempting to multiply the half-life by 3.]

Page 91: Risks from Nuclear Radiation

1 a) E.g. When radiation enters the body, it can collide with molecules in body cells causing ionisation *[1 mark]* which can damage or destroy the molecules / cause cell damage/cell death/cancer/radiation sickness *[1 mark]*.

b) i) Treatment (of cancer) using radiation *[1 mark]*.
ii) E.g. radiotherapists may wear lead aprons/stand behind lead screens during procedures *[1 mark]*.
iii) Any two from: E.g. always store radioactive material in a lead box when not in use *[1 mark]*. / Never allow skin contact with a radioactive source *[1 mark]*. / Always use tongs to hold radioactive sources *[1 mark]*. / Always hold radioactive sources at arm's length *[1 mark]*. / Keep radioactive sources pointed away from you *[1 mark]*.

c) i) E.g. nuclear workers wear full protective suits *[1 mark]*. / Workers use remote-controlled robot arms to carry out work with highly radioactive material *[1 mark]*.
ii) E.g. it can stay highly radioactive for a very long period of time *[1 mark]*. / It needs to be buried somewhere, and people often object to it being buried near where they live *[1 mark]*. / It needs to be buried somewhere, so you have to use sites that are geologically stable *[1 mark]*.

Page 92: Nuclear Fission

1 a) E.g. Uranium-235/U-235 *[1 mark]*
b) i) A slow-moving neutron gets absorbed by a uranium-235 nucleus causing it to split *[1 mark]*. The uranium nucleus will split to form two daughter nuclei *[1 mark]*, a small number of neutrons *[1 mark]* and a large amount of kinetic energy *[1 mark]*.
ii) In a nuclear reactor, the neutrons released from each fission event collide with other uranium nuclei causing other fission events that release more neutrons *[1 mark]*. This is known as a chain reaction *[1 mark]*. The nuclear reactor contains a moderator that slows down the neutrons released from fission so that they can successfully collide with uranium nuclei *[1 mark]*.
c) They limit the rate of fission by absorbing excess neutrons *[1 mark]*.

How to get answers for the Practice Papers

You can print out answers for the Practice Papers by accessing your free Online Edition of this book.
There's more info about how to get your Online Edition at the front of this book.

Equations Page

Here are some equations you might find useful when you're doing the practice papers — you'll be given these equations in the real exams.

orbital speed = $\dfrac{2\pi \times \text{orbital radius}}{\text{time period}}$	$v = \dfrac{2 \times \pi \times r}{T}$
$\dfrac{\text{energy}}{\text{transferred}}$ = current × voltage × time	$E = I \times V \times t$
frequency = $\dfrac{1}{\text{time period}}$	$f = \dfrac{1}{T}$
power = $\dfrac{\text{work done}}{\text{time taken}}$	$P = \dfrac{W}{t}$
power = $\dfrac{\text{energy transferred}}{\text{time taken}}$	$P = \dfrac{W}{t}$
pressure × volume = constant	$p_1 \times V_1 = p_2 \times V_2$

Assume the acceleration due to gravity is $g = 10$ m/s^2

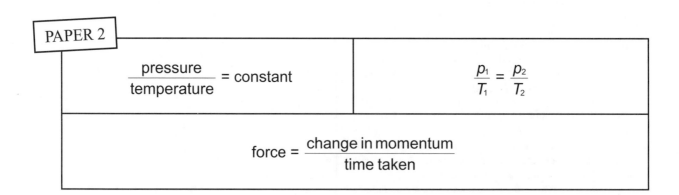

PAPER 2	
$\dfrac{\text{pressure}}{\text{temperature}}$ = constant	$\dfrac{p_1}{T_1} = \dfrac{p_2}{T_2}$
force = $\dfrac{\text{change in momentum}}{\text{time taken}}$	

PEQI41